# Strategic Concepts in Fire Fighting

**Edward P. McAniff**

John J. Cunningham, Editor

FIRE ENGINEERING "Leading the fire service since 1877"

a publication of
Technical Publishing,
a company of the
Dun & Bradstreet Corporation
New York

Second Printing 1983
by Fire Engineering
875 Third Avenue
New York, N.Y. 10022

Library of Congress Catalog Card No. 74—19536
ISBN 0-912212-02-0

Printed in the United States of America

# the author

Edward P. McAniff joined the New York City Fire Department in 1936 and attained all ranks, and retired as Chief of Department in 1965; Dean of Fire Promotion Courses at the Delehanty Institute, wherein 93% of the New York Fire Department officer personnel were educated in the fields of leadership, management, fire strategy and fire protection; author of two manuals for personnel training for Westinghouse Electric Corp.; developer of the fire protection features of the early-warning defense installation in the northern part of the western hemisphere; in charge of the U.S. Navy Fire Fighting School, Pearl Harbor, 1944-1946; director of seminars in fire strategy and leadership conducted for fire department personnel in many cities on the eastern seaboard; member of every major fire fighting and fire protection organization and a frequent principal speaker at their annual conventions. He was educated at Fordham University, St. John's University Law School and the N.Y.U. Graduate School of Public Administration.

# the editor

John J. Cunningham served in the New York City Fire Department for thirty-two years, progressing through the various ranks to Assistant Chief of Department, before retiring in 1969 as Director of the Management Planning Bureau. His latest publications are entitled *Oil Spills Control Manual for Fire Departments* and *A Rapidly Deployable Oil Containment Boom for Emergency Harbor Use,* published in 1973 by the U.S. Environmental Protection Agency. He was educated at the University of the City of New York and the N.Y.U. Graduate School of Public Administration.

# dedication

My wife Charlotte has assisted me extensively, over a period of thirty-five years in accomplishing my many objectives. Therefore, it is with great love and affection that I dedicate this book to her.

My life-long friend Charles F. Kirby has assisted me in many projects, and especially in contributing to this book.

# preface

Not only was my vocation firefighting, but it constituted my chief interest from 1936 to 1965. On retiring from the department, my aim was to write a series of books on fire strategy and tactics. This is the first such book; others will follow. In trying to learn my profession, I found good availability of information on the basic material for skill development of a firefighter. But I found a dearth of material on the principles of combatting fires. I was therefore intent on committing to writing those principles and concepts which helped to guide me in handling major fires.

To the unprofessional eye, it will appear that the solution to the problem at major fires is to surround and drown. Such would be the case if fires spread equally amid predictable geometrical designs, and task forces arrived majestically and instantaneously at well-defined sectors of the fire area. Such is not the case; the fire chief will find himself faced with a dynamic, rather than a static condition. Forces are usually limited at the time of the fastest fire spread. It is particularly at this stage of the fire that the strategist can be distinguished from the unskilled fire chief.

## art work

The author and editor are especially pleased with the illustrations and art work of Dave Hirsch and Henry Holzwarth.

## hose diameters

While this book was being compiled, the City of New York was experimenting with 1¾" diameter hose. This experiment has been so successful that for interior fire fighting the 1¾" hose has replaced 1½", and in most cases 2½" hose.

Therefore, throughout this book, when the author recommends 2½" hose (because of its large carrying capacity) the student must recognize that these new technological improvements have made 1¾" the equivalent of 2½" hose.

## the case method

Fire officers throughout the country generally do not have the opportunity to participate in actual fires with sufficient frequency to develop into well-rounded strategists. Therefore, they must develop their knowledge from the experiences of others. A most effective medium of training to accomplish this expertise is through the use of the case method. For the case method to be effective, the student must fully understand and visualize the fire situation before he develops his own strategy and tactics. When the student's plan of action has crystallized, the answers to the questions will become more meaningful. Fire situations vary, and some of the textbooks state that no two fires are exactly alike. But once a good understanding of fire science is developed, it will be noted that there are more similarities than differences in fires.

The case method is used extensively throughout this book. The student is counselled to refer to the accompanying drawings while assimilating the facts of the case. He should consider all aspects of the fire, especially the action taken by the first-arriving chief. He must keep in mind the concepts already discussed in this book in formulating his answer. Space is provided after each of the questions to enable the student to summarize the principal aspects of his answer.

Only by following these guide-lines can the student expect to fruitfully gain knowledge from the case method. There are no short-cuts to learning. All chiefs had to work hard to learn their profession; there are no exceptions.

# *texas city disaster*

This fire illustrates in a most forceful way the value of a fire department to its community. Furthermore, it demonstrates that the field of fire fighting should be restricted to professionals, i.e., men trained in the science and art of firemanics. Alexander Pope, in one of his famous couplets, wrote:

"A little knowledge is a dangerous thing,

Drink deep or touch not the Pyrian Spring."

How applicable the wisdom of this saying was to this fire.

In the Texas City Disaster, a simple fire on one ship resulted in the fifth largest conflagration in the history of the United States. A professional fire chief directing operations would have successfully controlled this fire and prevented the conflagration. There was an appalling loss of 552 lives, and over 3,000 personal injuries in a community of only 15,000 residents. The property loss exceeded $50,000,000.

## summary of fire

The fire was discovered in a cargo hold of the "Grandcamp" on the morning of April 14, 1947. The cargo included bagged ammonium nitrate fertilizer. The inception of the fire must have been small, because ship personnel were able to descend into the hold and closely approach the fire. They originally employed hand extinguishers. Then hose lines were lowered to them and used. But because of the fear of damaging the cargo, orders were issued to shut down the hose streams and withdraw. The crew went topside, the hatches were battened down and covered with tarpaulins. The ventilation cowls were blanked off, and then the steam smothering system was activated. Concomitant with these actions, the fire gained in proportions, and when the hatch covers blew off, the command to abandon ship was issued.

About 55 minutes from the inception of the fire, the "Grandcamp" distintegrated with a tremendous explosion. Shrapnel-like fragments of the ship's hull were hurled two to three thousand feet into the air. Some shrapnel travelled more than ten thousand feet. Burning balls of sisal showered the industrial and oil refinery areas. The downward thrust of the blast caused an unheaval of a huge wave of water of sufficient force to float a thirty-ton steel barge inland, and inundate the land area.

At 1:10 a.m. the next morning, another ship, the "Highflyer," detonated. It was loaded with a nitrate fertilizer and sulfur and other cargo. Red hot fragments of the ship's hull rained into the already devastated area, spreading and compounding the damage in general.

## municipal fire department

The personnel from the municipal fire department responded to the scene. They stretched many hose lines to the pier and were ready to take action, but they were made aware that the captain of a ship is its master. Legally, a ship's captain has full responsibility regarding its safety. The chief of a department is not allowed aboard the ship except with permission of the captain. So firefighters stood by and when the "Grandcamp" blew up, all of them died.

## ammonium nitrate

The manner of handling ammonium nitrate fires has been well established. It can only explode under certain set conditions; and is not generally classified as combustible. The two principal prerequisites for explosion are:

1.  High pressures

2.  High temperatures

Failure to use water streams allowed for progressive increases in temperature in the ship's hold. Shutting off the ventilating system and closing the hatches led to an increase in the pressure. An explosion therefore became inevitable. Conversely, if water is applied in great quantities using major streams, and ventilation is immediate (even if it means resorting to cutting the plates of the ship to dissipate the gases of combustion) the dangerous pressure build-up cannot occur.

U.S. General George S. Patton, through his mastery of the strategy and tactics of war, could turn the tide of a battle. Major fire disasters are similar to military battles. Both are sporadic, both seem inevitable. Fires can occur in almost any community throughout the United States. We, the members of fire departments, must be ready, like a Patton, to use strategy, tactics, leadership and scientific knowledge to achieve victory over fire. In so doing, the fire chief becomes the Patton of his community—the master strategist over our enemy—Fire.

## volunteer and paid chiefs

At the fire scene there is no distinction between a volunteer and a paid chief. Their responsibilities are equal. The saving of life and the protection of property recognizes no difference between the paid fire chief and the volunteer fire chief. Large fires occur in all of our communities, but naturally, they are more frequent in big cities. All chiefs must learn from the experience of others. But this is especially true of the fire chief in smaller communities. Fire strategy and tactics is a trade for the ignorant and a science for men of knowledge. Training is the difference.

*contents*

# Chapter

Chapter

Chapter

# illustrations

# Chapter 1

# Strategic Factors

Science is defined as a department of systematized knowledge. It is the endeavor of every professional in each of the scientific fields to catagorize his knowledge so that it falls into an orderly system. At the fire battleground, split-second decisions are constantly being made. Orders then flow down the chain of command. Once a decision is made, the die is cast. There are few opportunities for a second chance. Good decisions can only emanate from systemized knowledge. Therefore, students of fire strategy should be determined to classify their knowledge in such a way that correct decisions can readily flow from it.

The notion of the "strategic factor" was evolved by economists and businessmen about 30 years ago, and appeared in scientific circles as the "limiting factor."

Strategic (limiting) factors are factors or conditions of such strategic importance that the success of the entire operation depends on either overcoming their effect or keeping within the limits set by such factors. In some instances it is a factor, the elimination or control of which at the right time and right place, or in the right amount and right form, will establish a new, more favorable set of conditions. It may be a condition that acts as a

1

stumbling block, barring the way to efficient operations and rapid control of the fire. In other instances it may be a factor so critical, intransigent or unyielding that all operations must be modified to accommodate to the condition. In which case, it cannot be overcome; it must be accepted.

In fire terminology, certain factors have been established and defined, which assist the student of fire strategy in sizing up a particular fire situation. The analysis, or size-up, leads to the development of an operational plan for that fire. The size-up and operational plan will be discussed in Chapter Three.

On the other hand, identifying the one or two limiting factors will guide the chief in selecting the paramount actions for strategic or tactical success. By this identification, the chief frequently is able to immediately select the strategy most appropriate for the fire situation.

For example, in major church fires, the strategic factor is usually roof ventilation. If the roof ventilation is ample, the chief can often pursue an offensive attack on the fire. On the other hand, if roof ventilation is non-existent, the strategy becomes defensive.

Is this true of all major church fires? No, for in some instances the major church fire may be seriously exposing an occupied high-rise multiple dwelling. Then, of course, the strategic factor becomes the saving of life in the multiple dwelling. This, then, becomes the factor that will govern the chief in the overall command of this fire.

This is what makes the selection of strategy so difficult at fires. No textbook can enumerate all possible fires, and identify the strategic factor for each fire. The analysis must be made at the fire scene. Since present fire terminology has not fully categorized and defined the various types of fire strategies, and since verbal or written communication cannot be precise without well defined terms, the author will classify, define and illustrate the various types of fire strategy, as developed by him from his fireground and teaching experiences. This material will constitute Chapter Two.

The need for identification of the strategic factor is amply illustrated in a comparison analysis of the history of successfully fought fires and those which have resulted in tragedies or disasters. Some of these failures can be related to strategic error, such as the use of excessive quantities of water while ignoring the limiting factor of stability, in the case of some ship fires. No matter how dedicated, efficient, or large a fire department is, all its resources and dedication cannot rectify the error of a field commander who fails to recognize the limiting factors and wastes his resources on routine and possibly insignificant commitments.

But fortunately, along with the historical strategic errors in fire fighting have come strategic successes. Over the years, competent fire chiefs seem to have been able to evaluate serious fire situations intuitively and devise efficient conclusions. This intuitive ability seems to have been acquired by these outstanding individuals after years of long experience in very active fire areas. Needless to say, their elusive gift separated these outstanding strategists from their qualified but untalented peers.

One might conjecture that these strategists could deal with the many unknowns presented by varying fire situations through some kind of clairvoyance or extrasensory perception. Not only did they make fewer miscalculations on the fire grounds, but they got the essence of the fire problem and put first things first in deciding the parameters within which their operations plan would function. These field generals had the genius for recognizing the limiting or strategic factors presented by the fire situations they encountered.

To provide understanding of the strategic factor concept, three fire situations are presented in which the strategic factors are identified and the fire strategy is developed to fit this analysis. Throughout this book the strategic factor will be discussed in many fire situations. Since the concept is new in fire circles, the student will not firmly grasp it at first, but by the time he has completed this text, he will be thoroughly indoctrinated in identifying the strategic factors.

Figure 1.  *Serious outdoor fire exposes an occupied tenement and a frame church.*

## FIRE SITUATION—FRAME CHURCH—TENEMENT (Figure 1)

### *CHURCH*

A frame church of some historic importance is undergoing alterations, and portions of the wood siding have been removed and stored prior to disposal, in an alleyway between the church and an adjacent structure. The church building is 40 × 60 feet and about 70 feet high. The roof of the church has no skylights or other openings. The upper 20 feet comprise the cockloft space. The ceiling is of wood lath and heavy ornamental plaster. At the time of the fire, the church is unoccupied.

### TENEMENT

A five-story tenement, 25 × 60 feet, is 20 feet from the church. The tenement's exterior wall facing the church is unpierced on the first floor, but has windows on all other floors. The stairwell in the tenement is unenclosed and it has a well hole for its entire height. There are two apartments on each floor, one on the west and the other on the east side of the building. The tenement is occupied.

### FIRE

On arrival at 3 a.m. on a warm August night, heavy fire in a large pile of discarded lumber has already communicated to the church and the tenement, seriously exposing both structures. Fire spreads to the tenement stairway on upper floors.

### RESPONSE

Three engine and two ladder companies respond to the alarm.

1. *What orders would you issue to the officer in command of Engine 1? Engine 2? Engine 3? State reasons for each action.*

2. *Personnel of the two ladder companies as directed by the chief, made the necessary search and successfully remove all the tenants. Upon the arrival of second-alarm units, the first engine company stretches a line into the church, and then reports to the officer in command that the fire has raced through the exposed side wall of the church and is burning furiously in the cockloft. Other officers report extensive fire in the apartments on the upper floor of the tenement.*

   *Life is no longer a factor at this fire. There are two additional engine companies standing by, awaiting your orders. Would you assign them to the tenement or to the church structure? Give reasons.*

*3. What are the strategic factors?*

*1. Engine Co. 1*

A. Set up a heavy stream appliance to strike the lumber fire and to protect the windows of the tenement and church.

*Reasons*

This is the quickest means of getting water on the fire. The fire is massive, so we use a master stream. The convection and radiant heat must be controlled to wage an attack in any of the exposures. There is little hope of regaining and maintaining interior control in an exposure when openings are constantly being subjected to reignition from an undiminished parent body of fire.

B. Stretch to the interior of the tenement, directing the stream up the interior stairs.

*Reason*

To cool the upper regions of the building within the stairwell in the hope of maintaining the structural stability of the stairs, since this is the principal artery for rescue and line advancement operations.

C. Then advance to the second floor, darken fire in the west apartment. Direct stream out of the windows to cover lumber and church fires.

*Reasons*

First-floor exterior wall is unpierced at this location, so fire entry into the tenement will start at the second floor level. You will need a mass of water to control this fire situation. Therefore, the lines in the tenement, when feasible, should be used to augment the exterior heavy streams.

Since the tenement is occupied and the church is unoccupied, the original concentration of forces should be used to cope with the life hazard.

*Engine Co. 2*

A. Develop an additional heavy stream, preferably using a ladder pipe or elevating platform, and direct it on the lumber fire. Also, cover the tenement and church windows.
   *Reason*
   This is a quick way to increase the mass of water, and the ladder pipe or elevating platform will increase the height and distance of the stream.

B. Then stretch a line up the interior stairs. Cool the stairwell, especially at the upper floors, darken fire in the third floor west apartment and then project the stream toward the lumber and church fire.
   *Reason*
   Same as for Engine Company 1.

*Engine Co. 3*

A. Stretch up fire escape to the fourth floor.
   *Reason*
   There are already two lines on the interior stairs. To add another line is very likely to result in entanglement of hose and confusion in the stairwell.

B. Enter the apartment in the east side of the building and move toward and enter the stairwell.
   *Reason*
   This is a further effort to maintain the structural integrity of the stairs. If the company enters the apartment from the fire escape, there is the probability of pushing additional fire toward the stairwell.

    C. Cool stairwell at fourth and fifth floor levels, darken fire in fourth floor apartment facing lumber fire, and then project stream to cover lumber and church fire.
*Reason*
Same as Engine Companies 1 and 2.

2. The chief now has to make a decision whether to concentrate his remaining forces on the church, the tenement or both. Since the fire has extended into the fatal arteries of the church, an interior attack within this edifice is dangerous and doomed to failure. There is no ready means of ventilating the roof. To commit firemen to the roof for a cutting operation at this stage of the fire is extremely hazardous. Furthermore, the heavy ornamental plaster will fall from the ceiling and endanger the life of any fireman operating within the structure. This building is doomed. Therefore, the company is withdrawn.

   In the tenement, although there is a serious fire on the top floor, the interior stairs have been preserved and the physical arrangement of the individual apartments will restrict the rapid spread of fire.

   On this basis, a decision is made to save the tenement and use its position as a means of attack on the church fire. Of course, other heavy streams are strategically placed to control the church fire.

   Had reconnaissance shown that the fire had not advanced beyond control in the church, the chief would have concentrated his remaining forces on saving this historic church. The manpower already committed to the tenement could have successfully coped with the remaining fire within that structure.

3. The strategic factors in this fire are:
   A. Life hazard in the tenement
   B. Roof ventilation of the church

   Life is more fragile and infinitely more precious than property. Therefore, the first alarm forces concentrated on coping with the life hazard. So this strategic factor can be overcome by the proper assignment of companies.

The roof ventilation of the church was considered too dangerous under the stated conditions. Without roof ventilation, the church is doomed. Thus, this strategic factor cannot be overcome unless the lives of firemen are unnecessarily jeopardized. This fact must be accepted. The company is therefore withdrawn from the church interior.

Figure 2. *Barracks fire creating a severe radiant heat problem to a building storing explosives and a hangar building. Broken lines indicate radiant heat waves.*

**FIRE SITUATION—MILITARY POST (Figure 2)**

At a military post, a large vacant two-story frame barrack is heavily involved in fire and seriously exposing a similar building about 10 feet to the south. Somewhat to the east of both buildings is a frame warehouse storing high explosives. To the north of the explosives warehouse is a hangar for small military airplanes. A 5-mph wind is blowing from a south-easterly direction. The remaining area of the post is covered by occupied buildings, distant and not directly in the line of fire spread. Water supply consists of a single main capable of supplying about 800-gpm. There are two hydrants in the vicinity, one near the warehouse and the other close to the hangar. City mains circle the periphery of the post.

*ACTION TAKEN*

With a limited response of two engine companies, each manned by five men, the responding chief ordered the first pumper to connect to the hydrant near the warehouse building, and to stretch two 2¹/₂-inch lines with combination fog and solid stream nozzles to protect the structure storing the explosives.

The second engine company was ordered to connect to the hydrant near the hangar and to stretch a 2¹/₂-inch line with a 2¹/₂-inch combination nozzle to protect the hangar, and the men were to attempt to close the hangar door.

After the two buildings were properly cooled, the original lines were intermittently used to darken the fire in the barracks where the fire started and the adjacent vacant barracks to which the fire extended.

Additional arriving companies relayed water to the fire scene and positioned heavy streams to darken the original fire.

*QUESTIONS*

*1. Substantiate the strategy of the chief in command of this fire.*

2. *Is it advisable in this situation to use 2½-inch mobile lines or master stream appliances? Why?*

***ANSWERS***

1. The strategic factors in this fire are:
   A. Danger of conflagration and major life loss if the frame warehouse storing explosives detonates.
   B. Water supply only 800-gpm.

The chief must immediately grasp these strategic factors and plan his operations accordingly. At the inception of fire fighting, manpower and equipment are limited. The chief cannot, therefore, initiate and proceed with all operations simultaneously. The decision which faces the first-arriving officer is to make the most effective use of the forces available—doing first thing first. Since the barracks building is heavily involved in fire, radiant heat has already been absorbed by the walls and the roof of the warehouse and hangar. The first action must be the absorption of this heat, since these buildings have the greatest fire potential and have much greater significance than the two vacant barracks.

An urge to direct the first streams to cover the original fire building is the result of a tendency in fire circles to hit fire wherever it shows. If such inclinations prevail in this fire situation, the results may be catastrophic. Considerable radiant heat has been transmitted to the esposed buildings. As a result of these transmissions, the exposed buildings can erupt in flame or explosions. Since radiant heat is an invisible ray, the officer cannot accurately estimate its effects. Therefore, he cannot chance a direct attack on the fire. He has so little to gain and so much to lose.

2. The chief not only has limited companies and manpower, but limited water supply. He must keep his streams within the 800 gpm capacity of the water main system. Therefore, $2^{1}/_{2}$-inch lines were used rather than heavier streams from deck guns, deluge sets, etc., for these mobile lines will provide better coverage for the entire roof area of the exposures, as well as the walls facing the fire building. They can also be moved into the exposed buildings if the need arises. They can, furthermore, be moved toward the two barracks when the exposures have been secured.

### CONCEPT

*Protect exposures in the order of their importance.*

A. Give first consideration to life hazard.

B. Then give consideration to the exposure having the greatest potential fire development.

**FIRE SITUATIONS—ACE LUMBER COMPANY—MARINA (Figure 3) and (Figure 4)**

Figure 3.  *A massive lumberyard fire endangers a lumber ship and another lumberyard. Convected heat waves and fire brands reach across narrow river.*

*ACE LUMBER COMPANY*

A captain of an engine company responds to Box 35, which is in an outlying section of the community on the property of the Ace Lumber Company. Two other engine companies and a ladder company are assigned to respond to this box but will not reach the scene for another 5 or 10 minutes because of long distances, poor roads and bad weather.

Several large piles of lumber are burning vigorously. There is a 15 mph southerly wind.

The Bay Lumber Company is on the other side of a narrow river. Ships and barges are tied up to bulkhead buildings.

*What is the most important immediate action for the engine company captain to take? Give your reasons.*

A marina in a small bay or inlet consists of several small piers, a boat repair shed and a motel. There is also a gasoline storage barge anchored in the center of the bay. The marina is enclosed on the land side by a chain link fence and the only access is by means of a large gate. There are no hydrants or drafting positions inside the marina, but a narrow macadam road within the property leads to all piers and major buildings.

Figure 4. (1) *Burning pier—origin of fire.* (2) *Moored boats.* (3) *Exploding boats.* (4) *Boatel.* (5) *Other exposures.* (6) *Hydrants.* (7) *Road to Marina.*

*FIRE*

On your arrival, fire has full possession of the 30 x 60-foot pier, nearest the inlet and the wind is carrying sparks and dense smoke across the marina to the exposed buildings as shown in Figure 4. Several small craft are burning adrift and exploding.

*RESPONSE*

Three engine companies and one ladder company respond.

*QUESTION*

*The officer in command, after a quick size-up, transmits a radio request for a fifth-alarm response. This will provide an additional response of 12 engine companies. State the justification for this action.*

*ANSWERS—Ace*
*Lumber Company Fire*

The captain must immediately radio directions to the responding units to proceed to the north side of the river to protect the stored lumber, buildings, barges and ships of the Bay Lumber Company. The captain must also transmit greater alarms, and endeavor to darken and limit spread of fire by use of master stream appliances.

If the condition is not anticipated, the great number of small fires that are sure to originate in the lumberyard on north side of the river will merge into another large body of fire. A characteristic of a lumberyard fire is the large size of the brands which will travel with the wind. This necessitates establishing a brand-hazard control on the lee side of the fire with walkie-talkie communication to the chief in charge of the fire. In addition, stretch lines to drench combustible material exposed to convection currents and radiant heat.

*ANSWER—Marina Fire*

The chief sees the situation as it is at present—a 30 × 60-foot pier fully involved and several small craft burning and adrift. The wind is blowing sparks, brands and convection heat across the narrow inlet to similar structures.

Now he must envision what might occur. The hydrants are remote, the stretching will be slow and fatiguing. He has need for many 2¹/₂-inch lines and heavy stream appliances. The motel must be evacuated. Fire boats or private boats will have to be manned. The gasoline barge must be protected or removed from inlet and the drifting burning craft must be safely secured. Manpower will quickly tire as a result of the long stretches and exposure to dense smoke and heat, since most of the action will be on the leeward side of the fire.

The strategic factor in the Ace Lumber Company fire and the Marina fire relates to anticipating major spread of the fire before it occurs. The novice chief will transmit greater alarms as he sees the fire develop. The strategist, on the other hand, is a prognosticator. He anticipates developments and takes action before the occurrence. He calculates his apparatus and manpower needs, not on the basis of the present situation, but rather on the basis of the anticipated situation.

*CONCEPT*

In protecting exposures, set up defenses in anticipation of conditions, rather than wait for the emergency to reach more serious proportions.

# Chapter 2

# Fire Strategies

There are five basic classifications of fire-fighting strategies. They are:

1. Offensive
2. Offensive-defensive
3. Defensive-offensive
4. Defensive
5. The indirect method of attack.

Each of these types of strategies will be defined and a fire situation presented to provide understanding of the definition. However, the indirect method of attack will be presented in a later chapter.

One of the fire situations to be presented will show strategy modifications which take place at many of the major fire situations. The original strategy may be offensive, but if the fire situation continues to deteriorate, the strategy may move through the various types to become purely defensive. The reverse can also take place.

## OFFENSIVE

A direct attack is made on the seat of the fire or on the immediate area involved in fire. The offensive strategy is the strategy most commonly employed since, upon arrival, most fires are of rather small extent or can be attacked directly before the fire extends.

Its greatest virtue is that all problems are solved at one time—life safety, confinement and extinguishment. Its essence is a close-up attack, aggressively fought and aggressively followed up by whatever forces are required.

## OFFENSIVE-DEFENSIVE

This strategy embodies a vigorous attack against the main body of fire, while taking adequate measures to control actual and potential extension of fire. The major portion of the fire force operates directly on fire extinguishment problems and a lesser force on fire extension problems. This is the common strategy at fires in the "all hands" or second alarm stages when rapid control of the fire seems promising.

## DEFENSIVE-OFFENSIVE

This is essentially a "holding action" to keep the fire within reasonable bounds while awaiting the availability of additional forces. These additional forces may be either additional companies that are called or units at the fire that will shortly become available upon completion of their initial assignments.

## DEFENSIVE

In this strategy, all forces are heavily engaged in defensive actions. Typically, it would be used when the volume of fire and the number and nature of exposures preclude anything but defensive techniques. Any offensive content that may be present in such defensive techniques as heavy streams, lacks the dynamic, advancing qualities we associate with offensive strategies.

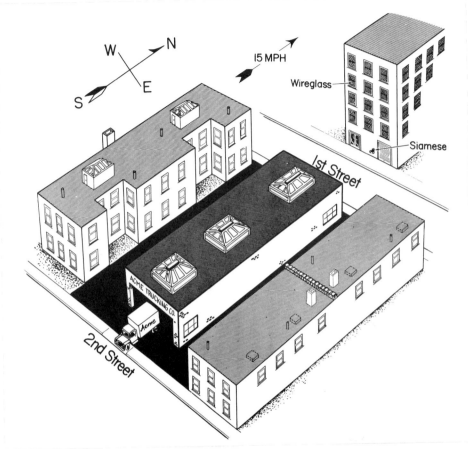

Figure 1. *Garage fire demonstrating application of offensive strategy.*

## OFFENSIVE STRATEGY—GARAGE FIRE EXPOSING MANY OTHER BUILDINGS (Figure 1)

In the early hours of the morning, a fire is reported in the rear portion of a one-story garage with a large entrance doorway. Trucks are stored neatly against the brick side and rear walls. The roof is of open heavy timber construction with three large skylights. Twenty feet to the west is a group of two-story, garden-type apartments with many windows facing the garage. To the north is a five-story factory, storing foam rubber toys and assorted combustible stock. This building is fireproof, fully sprinklered and protected by wire glass windows. To the east are two old non-fireproof paper warehouses connected on each floor by two fire doors.

On arrival, smoke is issuing from the garage door and a red glow is noted at the rear skylight near the west wall of the building. Tenants vacating the garden-type apartments report that some of the families on the second floor are old and infirm and need assistance.

*ACTION TAKEN*

The first-arriving chief, aware that the dwelling constitutes the only severe life hazard, orders two engines to stretch lines into the dwelling and assigns his ladder units to assist in the removal of the tenants. The chief orders the third engine to direct a deck pipe over the roof toward the rear of the garage, and he also requests a second alarm.

On the arrival of a second-alarm assignment, fire is reported venting through the rear skylight. In addition, the dispatcher notifies the chief that a valve alarm has been received from the factory in the rear of the fire building.

Based on these reports and aware of the wind direction, the chief transmits a third alarm and assigns all second-alarm units to report to the front of the factory entrance on the next street. A higher ranking chief, arriving with the third-alarm units, notes that the fire has vented through the rear half of the roof, that a portion of the roof is collapsing and that vehicle gas tanks are exploding. He orders two deluge sets to be operated at the garage doorway entance and hand lines stretched by third-alarm units into the floors of the paper warehouse at the east.

Calling for reports, he is informed that the dwelling has been evacuated safely and that sufficient lines are operating from windows to assure coverage of this building. At the factory building to the north, the report is that some sprinklers are operating but that no fire has entered the building and that one large pumper is supplying lines into the sprinkler siamese. The ladder units in the dwelling are reassigned to the paper warehouses to close fire doors, vent judiciously and aid in directing streams onto the east side of the garage roof. Shortly thereafter, the fire is darkened down and the situation is placed under control.

## QUESTIONS

*1. This fire was handled poorly. What was the primary strategic failure in commanding this fire? State reasons.*

*2. What factors misguided the commander in developing the original strategy?*

*3. Properly assign Engine 1, stating the purpose or expected accomplishments of this engine company.*

*4. Properly assign Engine 2, stating the purpose or expected accomplishment of this engine company.*

*5. Properly assign Ladder 1, stating the purpose or expected accomplishments of this ladder company.*

*6. Why would it be inadvisable for the members of the first engine company to wear self-contained breathing apparatus at this particular fire?*

7. *Properly assign Engine 3, stating the purpose or expected accomplishment of this engine company.*

8. *Discuss the advantages and disadvantages of transmitting greater alarms or calling for additional companies at the time of arrival of the first-due chief.*

*ANSWERS*

1. Criticism: The strategy of the first commander was one of defense, rather than offense.

   *Reasons*

   A. The strategic factors at this situation are that the fire was localized, with excellent features of ventilation and accessibility. This dictates an offensive strategy. The large entrance doorway, the open area in the center of the garage and the open beamed ceilings all would be favorable to the effectiveness of interior hose streams. Large skylights on the roof would permit venting to localize the fire and assure the removal of heat and smoke ahead of the advancing lines.

   B. Hit the main body of fire and all other problems diminish. This concept should be foremost in the mind of the officer first to arrive on the scene. There are many factors that require consideration at a fire threatening to extend. In the early stages, you are limited in manpower and resources. The successful strategist will concentrate his manpower where decisive blows can be struck and risk being at a disadvantage at defensive points. The success of offensive moves far outweighs defensive tactics. Defensive tactics lead to an element of defeat. You lose the fire building while trying to save the exposure when you could be saving both. On first-alarm operations, try insofar as possible, to retain the offensive against a fire.

2. Poor evaluation of information given to the chief seemed to have an adverse effect on the selection of his strategy. A report of old and infirm people in the dwelling caused him to assign most of his first-alarm units in that direction—a defensive tactic. A report of a valve alarm in the factory caused him to send all second-alarm units to the rear street—another defensive tactic. Evaluate the facts in reference to your experiences. You are the professional and you should determine strategy. It is far too common for chief officers to be bombarded with worthless and misleading information and advice.

3. Assignment, Engine Company 1: Stretch a 2½-inch line to the front entrance of the garage.
   *Purpose:*
   Move line toward fire area, darken and extinguish fire.

4. Assignment, Engine Company 2:
   A. Assist Engine 1 in stretching.
   B. Then stretch a 2½-inch line to back up Engine 1.
   *Purpose:*
   A. To expedite the stretch and to get water on fire as quickly as possible.
   B. The second line increases the cooling capabilities of the attack force. It will be a substitute line in case of a burst hose in the first line.

5. Assignment, Ladder Company 1: Remove skylights over fire area. Open or break windows in rear and west walls of garage in the vicinity of the fire.
   *Purpose:*
   These ventilation procedures will permit smoke and heat to flow from building, thus making it easier for the engine men to advance their lines.

6. A. It takes time to don them.
   B. It slows down the stretching.
   C. It reduces visibility.
   D. Ceilings are high, ventilation opportunies are good, the wind is at their backs. They don't need them.

7. Assignment, Engine Company 3: Stretch a 2¹/₂-inch line to the northwest area of the fire building, exterior stream.
   *Purpose:*
   1. To protect dwelling in case fire breaks through windows or skylights.
   2. If Engine 1 fails to advance its line, use stream through windows to cool fire. In this case, however, Engine 1 must be warned to withdraw temporarily. The exterior stream will be used only momentarily, then shut down, and Engine 1 will be ordered to advance.

8. Unfavorable factors:
   A. Engine Company 1 must move at least 50 feet into garage to hit fire.
   B. The possibility of gasoline tank explosions.
   C. The close spacing of buildings.
   D. The life situation as reported in the dwelling.
   E. The garage is nonfireproof, large, and undivided.
   F. A moderately strong wind.
   G. Both warehouses are old and nonfireproof.

9. Favorable Factors:
   A. On arrival the fire is only in a corner of the building.
   B. On arrival, the fire has not broken through windows or skylights. Therefore, very high temperatures have not been attained.
   C. There is good access to the fire from the front of the building.
   D. Ceilings are high and with adequate ventilation. The floor temperatures should be near normal.
   E. The wind will push smoke and heat away from advancing firemen.
   F. Since the garage is only one story high, vertical extension is not a problem.

G. The most serious exposure is fireproof, sprinklered, and has windows of wire glass.

### CONCLUSION:

A. With proper coordination of ventilation and line advancement, this fire should be extinguished in a matter of minutes.
C. Life and exposure problems can be covered with one engine company.
D. All fires are fraught with certain dangers. There is a possibility of explosion of gasoline tanks. You must distinguish between possibilities and probabilities. Otherwise, you will be transmitting unnecessary greater alarms at a frequent rate. If you vent the building properly and immediately, and put enough manpower on the first line to expedite the stretch, the probability is that the gas tanks will not explode.

## OFFENSIVE—DEFENSIVE STRATEGY—An Apartment or Tenement House Fire

A four-story tenement building is 20 × 60 feet in area. The exterior walls are brick, the floor beams wood, and the interior partitions are wood lath and plaster. The stairs are of wood, enclosed in wood lath and plaster partitions. A roof bulkhead is provided over the stairs. There are two families on each floor.

### FIRE SITUATION

The fire originates on the second floor, and involves three rooms of a six-room apartment. The gases of combustion and the flames have already vented into a light and air shaft which is open at roof level. There is a fire escape on the rear of the building. There is a southerly wind of 30 mph. The building has been completely evacuated of tenants.

*1. What is the strategic factor that guides the fire chief in the development of his strategy for this fire?*

*2. Discuss why the atmosphere in the fire apartment reaches furnace-like temperatures.*

*3. Discuss the shaft situation at time of arrival.*

4. *Why is it so essential that a hose line be immediately taken to the seat of the fire to hit the mass of fire?*

5. *The engine men are endeavoring to move a line with a combination fog and solid stream nozzle through a long hallway to the rooms of the fire apartment. Although they are equipped with self-contained breathing apparatus, the heat barrier is so great that their forward progress has been stopped, and they are now lying on the floor within the hallway, unable to come to grips with the fire. Why is this so?*

6. *Three engine companies respond on the first alarm to this fire situation. Each company is manned by five men. Should the three engine companies simultaneously stretch lines to positions directed by the chief?*

*7. What diameter hose should be stretched at this fire? Discuss.*

*8. Suppose the fire is blowing out the front windows. Discuss the use of outside streams in this fire situation.*

*9. Some chief officers advocate an initial response of one engine and one ladder company in the builtup sections of a city. Upon arrival, the officer is to evaluate the situation and send in calls for additional apparatus in accordance with his size-up. What effect would a one and one response have on this fire situation?*

*ANSWERS*

1. The chief is guided by the presence of a light-air shaft capable of extending fire to the upper floors of the fire building and to the exposed building across the shaft. The shaft therefore becomes the focal point of the fire control strategy. (Figure 2) The objective is to hit the mass of fire on the second floor—an offensive maneuver. Protect against major extension via the shaft—a defensive maneuver. So actually the strategy becomes one of the offensive-defensive type.

2. Since the fire is venting up the light and air shaft, there is a great inflow of oxygen into the fire apartment. The more rapid the velocity of the escaping gases of combustion, the

Figure 2. *Fire enters light and air shaft through window openings and frequently extends to rooms in both buildings.*

more rapid will be the inflow of new oxygen. The rate of velocity accelerates as the building materials in the shaft become heated.

3. The shaft has limited capacity, and since the volume of gases doubles for each increase of 459° F, the shaft's capacity is being taxed. The draft is always upward. The highly heated products of combustion are looking for other channels. Since all the windows in the shaft are plain glass, the intense heat will cause them to crack and fail. Since the volume of gases is seeking new channels, the flow will be to many of the rooms bordering on the shaft. If the doors to the apartments above are open, the convection currents will carry the heated products through the rooms to the public halls and stairway. If the doors are closed, generally there are only small fires in the curtains, shades, etc. near the windows bordering the shaft. If the curtains or shades fall on bedding, further spread of fire will occur.

4. In this type of combustible construction and in similarly constructed buildings, it must be realized that if the fire is not darkened within 10 or 15 minutes, it will burn through the ceiling and floor and, in a substantial manner, involve the apartment immediately above. Let this occur and the fire officer is in real trouble in his endeavors to control the fire. Dwell on this point for a moment and try to anticipate the developments. If a line on the second floor has not darkened the fire, a line on the third floor will not be able to move into the flat and control extension on this floor. No matter what the capacity of the fire fighters is, it is physically impossible to move a line above the fire under these conditions. Movement will take place only after the fire has been darkened on the second floor. Experienced firefighters soon recognize the fact that in non-fireproof construction, the fire floor is a more comfortable position than the floor above.

5. When fire attains a vigorous level of combustion, temperatures elevate rapidly. Temperatures of 1200° F at the ceiling level and 300 degree at the five-foot level are not uncommon. These temperatures are fatal to humans. Therefore, as the

line advances, the water must cool the atmosphere and the convection currents must flow away from the advancing firemen. If the line is moving from the front, there must be adequate openings in the rear to exhaust the convection heat. However, with a southerly wind of 30 miles an hour, the flow of the products of combustion will be from the rear to the front of the building.

In this type fire, generally the first two engine companies stretch to the interior of the building via the interior stairs. When wind conditions halt the advancement of lines, one of the engine companies is redirected and ordered to bring its line up the rear fire escape and into the second floor apartment. The company will work toward the shaft to cool it. As the shaft is cooled, the velocity of the escaping gases will diminish and, concurrently, the inflow of oxygen to the fire apartment will abate. This line will also be wetting the window frames on the upper floors.

6. Since time is the critical factor in successful fire extinguishment, efficiency at fires is very closely related to the proper use of manpower with the objective of quickly getting a line to the seat of the fire.

Where three engine companies respond to a fire of first-alarm proportions, some officers will have each of the engine companies stretch its own hand line. This has the appearance of efficiency in that all men are busily engaged. But it is hard work to stretch hose lines up interior stairs, ladders, fire-escapes or through adjoining buildings. A considerable amount of a company's momentum is lost before it even reaches the fire area; and its biggest job is yet to be done. The officer should keep in mind the fatigue factor of men. Stretch the minimum number of lines compatible with fire conditions and maintain movement in these lines.

The manpower of the first two engine companies should be used to get the first line operational. Time is the biggest factor. If the fire burns through the ceiling and floor above, this fire will reach third and fourth alarm proportions. If this occurence can be prevented, this situation can at times be controlled with first-alarm companies, plus an additional company or two. Of course, if the ladder companies leave the hallway doors open to apartments on upper floors in fire and adjoining buildings, the fire extension will be too great to control with first alarm units.

7. **HOSE DIAMETERS**

There are hundreds of different wrenches manufactured. The one to use depends upon the job to be performed. And so, too, with hose lines. When fire is blowing out of windows or has reached the flashover point, the engine companies cannot advance unless they have a major stream in front of them. There is no protection against heat in these situations except adequate water.

With the improvement in fog streams, the $1^1/_2$-inch line has become more formidable. Of course, it has the advantages of quick stretching, mobility, and lightness. But have you ever been in a position where the door to the fire apartment was forced, and the engine company, equipped with a $1^1/_2$-inch fog nozzle, took two steps backward for every step forward? Since the fire apartment was in the process of being ventilated, the heat condition became so devastating that even a $2^1/_2$-inch line had difficulty in advancing. This is a case where the mass of water from the $1^1/_2$-inch line was not adequate to cope with the generated heat. There are many similar cases.

In fighting fire in apartment buildings, the $2^1/_2$-inch line has serious deficiencies, too. With adequate manpower, it can be stretched quickly and moved from floor to floor. But when making sharp bends, as when going from a hallway into a fire apartment, the weight and the stiffness of the hose slow advancement considerably. Fires have been lost for this reason.

The 1½-inch hose has the flexibility, but at time it delivers inadequate water; while the $2^1/_2$-inch hose provides adequate water under most conditions, it lacks the element of flexibility where sharp bends have to be maneuvered for advancement. It is for this reason that, in New York City, $1^1/_2$-inch hose with the three-quarter inch fog stream is gradually being eliminated in favor of $1^3/_4''$ nose with $^{15}/_{16}''$ nozzles. This apparently insignificant change attains an increase from 100 to 155 gpm with a nozzle pressure of 36 psi.

All pumpers now being purchased by New York City will be equipped to use Rapid Water in everyday operations. The research on 1³/₄-inch hose and Rapid Water covered a five-year period. The efficiency attained through this program has been phenomenal.

The 1¾-inch hose with the ¹⁵/₁₆-inch nozzle, with or without Rapid Water has already proven to be thoroughly adequate for interior fire-fighting in this and similar fire situations.

8. Outside streams are generally not advisable in this type of fire situation. Once a heavy exterior stream is opened, offensive operations come to a standstill, and the impact of the heavy stream can, under certain conditions, drive high heat and smoke toward the fire fighters and tenants, placing them in serious personal jeopardy.

    Therefore, an exterior stream is a last resort and is only used after you have exhausted all the procedures for interior fire fighting. The purpose of the exterior stream is to cool the original fire area so that interior lines can rapidly advance into this area. Since the rooms in apartment and tenement houses are relatively small and the exterior streams are limited in their penetration, the cooling process can be accomplished in a period of seconds, not minutes. The exterior line is then shut down, and offensive operations are resumed.

    An important admonition in this matter is to be sure to provide opportunity for notification to all forces within the building to withdraw to safe locations while exterior streams are in operation.

9. There will be inadequate manpower and apparatus to cope with extension possibilities. The fire building is sure to be lost and the exposed buildings are in serious jeopardy. If the buildings are occupied at the time of arrival of fire units, there is inadequate manpower and ladder equipment for rescue and search procedure.

Most of the fires are in the incipient state at the time of arrival of fire apparatus. An extinguisher or a small hand line will usually control the situation. The incipient fire requires little skill and respresents no unusual challenge to the fire force. But about 5 percent of the fires are either major fires at the time of arrival or developing into major situations. It is in these fire situations that fire departments render the best service to their community. These are the fires where lives are saved by the fire fighting forces, and the fire fighters, through their determination and skill, prevent further extension.

When the fire forces start operating at a fire, they are, in addition to stretching hose lines, ventilating the fire area. This is the critical stage of fire fighting, for with the increase in ventilation the fire will progress unless water is immediately applied to the flaming area. This is the time the companies must be at the fire scene—not five minutes later. Wage a strong offensive attack, for once the building has been ventilated, the time for effective fire extinguishment is limited. Regrettably, in some of our cities the false alarm problem has become so taxing that responses are reduced for economic reasons. The reduced response programs attempt to assure availability of fire companies for subseqeunt alarms. But in congested sections of a city, where construction is deficient and permits a rapid spread of fire to upper floors, a reduced response is sure to lead to unnecessary fire extension, additional life jeopardy, and many greater alarm situations.

## DEFENSIVE—OFFENSIVE STRATEGY—SUPERMARKET FIRE

### DESCRIPTION OF BUILDING

The building is one-story and basement, occupied as a grocery supermarket. The dimensions are 100 x 100 feet. There are two interior stairways about 30 feet from the front of the building. One of the stairs is on the west wall; the other is on the east

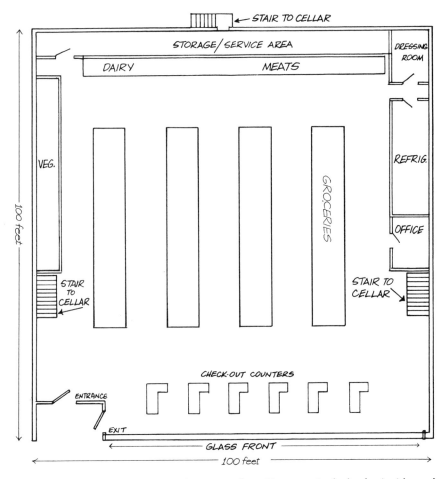

Figure 3.   *Plan of first floor of supermarket. Note particularly the inside and outside cellar stairs.*

wall. There is a rear basement door, and there are exterior windows on the rear and side walls of the basement. There are large show windows in the front of the building. (Figure 3)

### FIRE SITUATION

The fire is confined to the basement. Heavy smoke and intense heat are venting up the interior stairs. The time is 2:00 a.m. (Figure 4)

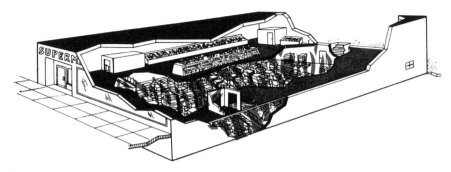

**Figure 4.** *Cutaway shows extent of fire in basement. Fire has not entered first floor.*

*QUESTIONS*

1. *The first and second engine companies were ordered to stretch 2½-inch lines to the first floor to protect against fire extension at the interior stairs. This is a defensive-offensive strategy. Discuss.*

2. *Under the conditions stated in the question, is it advisable for Engine Company 1 or Engine Company 2 to try to move down the interior stairs to hit the fire?*

3. *After laddering the building, the personnel of Ladder Company 2 are assigned to the roof of the supermarket. What are their duties? Give reasons.*

4. *Presume that at the present time there is no fire in the cockloft. State where the roof cut should be made and why.*

5. *With the advent of power-saws in fire departments, trench cuts have become an established method of limiting fire extension in cockloft. There is no fire in the cockloft in this supermarket fire, and yet it is advisable to make a trench cut immediately after cutting the roof for ventilation. Why?*

6. *On arrival at this fire, should the first officer transmit a second alarm? Give reasons.*

7. *What does the term 'taxpayer' mean?*

8. *Why do taxpayer and supermarket fires plague almost every community?*

9. *Where there is early notification of fire, such as during business hours, a line can usually be brought to the scene of the fire and the flames can be extinguished. However, when the fire occurs at night, flame is roaring throughout the occupancy, the fire has vented itself through the roof, and even the sky appears illuminated, then the fire department is on the defensive and the forces are employed primarily to protect exposures and control the rate of burning in the building. Why use a defensive strategy?*

10. *There is a particular type of fire situation that occurs in these occupancies where the commander has an opportunity to exercise all his acumen in strategy and tactics. This is a pleasurable situation for a chief officer. He does not have that feeling of helplessness that prevails in situations where he is merely pouring water on the fire from exterior positions and is awaiting the collapse of the structure.*

*The type of fire now being discussed occurs at night. The building is closed and the fire has been burning for a long time. There is a considerable buildup of heat in the fire area and the cockloft. But since the inflow of oxygen is limited, too much flame is not visible and the roof remains in tact. To be sure, heavy smoke prevails and, if you put your face into the smoke, you will note the intense heat. Explain the strategy and tactical procedures which will guide the commander at this fire operation.*

1. The strategic factors in the supermarket fire relate to the large body of fire in the basement which is threatening to extend to the upper floor. If the chief can hold the fire to the basement until the arrival of additional companies, he may successfully control and extinguish this fire. Therefore, his first consideration is to defend against the spread of the fire to the first floor. This is essentially a holding action to keep the fire within reasonable bounds while awaiting the availability of additional forces. Therefore, the emphasis is on the defensive, but as soon as the second alarm companies arrive at the scene, they are assigned to the basement level. This constitutes an offensive maneuver. The overall strategy is, therefore, of the defensive-offensive type. The flow of orders to the companies is relatively easy once strategy has been established. The chief knows he must first confine the fire and then extinguish it. Therefore, the first companies will be above the fire to confine it, while later companies will constitute the extinguishing force.

2. The answer is a resounding "no." The principle which governs in this situation is "where fire is sizable, attack from the fire level or a lower level."

   *Explanation*
   It is folly to try to descend into a major fire area down the artery through which intense heat is rising. To send men down interior stairs to fight a major cellar fire is unnecessarily jeopardizing their lives. It is, to be sure, the quickest means of getting to the seat of the fire and chief officers have used it to bring fires quickly under control. But the fire fighting task was accomplished regardless of the hardship it imposed upon the human spirit. The tyrannical chief had a simple fire strategy. Locate the fire and, regardless of conditions, force companies to proceed to the seat of the fire. There are always alternative ways of performing a task. Select the one which will accomplish the goals, but let the method be compatible with the safety of personnel.

   In below level fires, such as cellars, subways and ship holds, the effort should be toward descending to fire level,

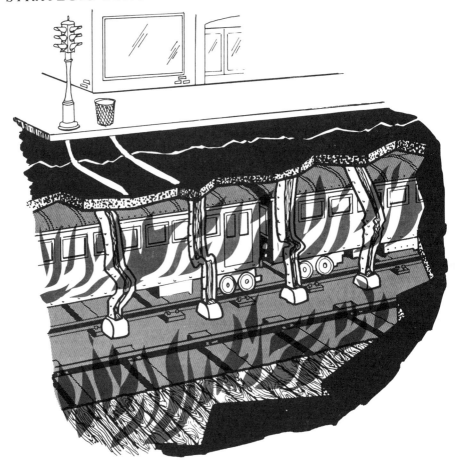

Figure 5. *Note buckling of steel supporting columns. If fire had continue much longer street would have collapsed into subway.*

or below, from a remote and safe area and then moving the hose lines toward the seat of the fire. A case in point is a subway fire, which occurred in New York City on April 21, 1964. Dense, black, extremely hot smoke with occasional showers of sparks was belching upward from the subway ventilating grates. All six direct entrances to the immediate fire area were venting thick clouds of superheated smoke. The fire was three levels below the street and involved trains, the wooden sections of the platforms, and the ties and grease on the tracks. Convected and radiated heat, as well as direct flame, spread the fire on three *mezzanine* levels to transit booths, turnstiles, a restaurant and a lunchroom. (Figure 5)

The tactical procedure in coping with this situation consisted of finding an entrance to the subway, in this case approximately two blocks away, where the descent was relatively free of heat. A line was advanced with the assistance of three engine companies. Additional men were assigned with rolled up lengths to extend the advancing line. As this line moved forward, additional lines were dropped to the subway level through ventilating grates in coordination with the original line.

This fire was so intense that the unprotected metal columns buckled and the street surface above sank from 8 to 10 inches. Nevertheless, there were no smoke inhalation cases or major injuries, and an efficient extinguishment job resulted.

3. Immediately and completely ventilate at the roof level. This involves removal of skylights, cutting the roof to ventilate the cockloft and using any other available means of ventilation.

*Reasons*

A. The first floor will prove to be untenable for firefighting personnel unless very adequate ventilation is provided, since the smoke is heavy and the heat intense.

B. Roof ventilation will also improve the chances of engine company advancement into the basement area from the rear door.

C. Opening the cockloft provides a ready means for reconnaissance for upward fire travel.

D. If the companies can originally confine this fire to the basement, the extinguishment of the basement fire will be relatively easy, since there is good access and ventilation.

E. By the nature of their operations, certain officers and members find themselves in strategic positions for gaining important facts concerning the fire that are not directly available to the officer in command of the fire. Ladder company members operating on the roof during initial operations have unusually good opportunities to determine the depth and shape of the fire building, conditions and access to the rear, and the nature and severity of exposures.

Company officers operating at the rear or in exposed buildings often have information of importance to the commanding officer. Favorable features are sometimes as important as unfavorable features. Many situations have both a favorable and unfavorable aspect. If the condition is discovered in time, the commander with initiative and skill can exploit the favorable aspect. If the condition is overlooked, not reported, or poorly handled, the unfavorable aspect may develop into a major problem. Therefore, it is essential to have a system for getting important information to the officer in command in time to be of value.

The ladder company officer must report by walkie-talkie the depth of the structure as well as the location of any parapeted walls. The report should include all the salient points, good and bad, seen from the roof that will assist the chief in developing tactical procedures. This report should be made within five minutes of the ladder officer's arrival at the roof area.

4. The cut should be made in the center of the roof, and 30 feet from the front of the building. In order for the firefighters to maintain their position on the first floor, smoke and heat issuing from both of the interior stairways will have to be vented at the roof level. One opening at the center of the roof can properly ventilate above the stairways, and the lateral movement of the smoke will be kept to a minimum.

5. The roofs of these buildings, without fire, are spongy. The roof boards nailed to the rafters generally are only three-fourths of an inch thick. If possible, whatever roof work is necessary should be done immediately upon the arrival of firefighters. The longer the procrastination, the greater the danger.

There is a heavy body of fire in the basement. There are

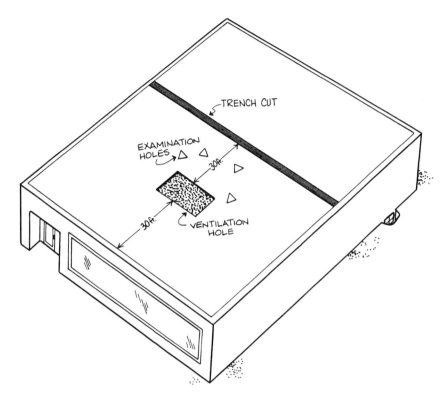

Figure 6.   *The ventilation opening in the roof should be as large as your car.*

channels for fire travel from basement to roof level. Anticipate the worst, for that is what generally develops in these buildings.

If fire did reach the cockloft space at the rear of the building, the buoyant gases of combustion would naturally flow toward the vent opening. Seventy percent of the roof area could be involved in fire. This would mean a change in strategy to a defensive operation, for the building would be doomed.

To prevent this, make a two-foot wide trench cut across the width of the roof about 30 feet back from the vent opening. This will limit the spread of the fire and perhaps keep it within a dimension that can be controlled.

Some chiefs would be reluctant to cut the roof so extensively, since there is no fire in the roof space, and this appears to be unnecessary property damage. The value of the roof compared to the rest of the building and its contents is minimal—probably less than 1 percent of the total value of building and contents.

These trench cuts have been used with great success not only in supermarket fires, but also in taxpayers, contiguous frame buildings and top floor fires in non-fireproof construction. Take advantage of shafts, skylights and bulkheads when planning the location of the trench cut. The length of the cut can be shortened by using these construction features.

Examination openings should be made in conjunction with the trench cut. These triangular cuts, the size of a power saw blade, will indicate the direction of fire travel. These openings are useful in establishing the best location for a trench cut, and the engine companies should use them to check fire extension with bent tip nozzles.

Do not put an umbrella of water above or within the vent opening. This is always a wrong procedure when waging an interior attack. The engine men below have to withdraw from the building if roof ventilation is not provided for them. The umbrella of water at the vent opening negates roof ventilation.

6. The favorable factor in this fire situation is that at the time of arrival of the first alarm units, the fire is confined to the basement area, yet the smoke and heat indicate a sizable fire. The fire officer can predict further extension unless the attack is vigorous and prompt. The emphasis so far has been on confinement, but this strategy will fail unless water is applied to the fire at the basement level. Unfortunately, the fire cannot originally be attacked at the basement level without causing its extension to the upper regions of the building.

With two engine and two ladder units assigned to defensive operations, additional companies are immediately needed for offensive operations at the basement level. Furthermore, the ladder personnel will fatigue readily because of their many arduous tasks, and all personnel will need relief because of the smoke and heat.

The engine and ladder personnel are standing on an inferno. Time is of the essence. Help is needed immediately. Therefore, transmit a greater alarm on arrival so that positions can be reinforced, lines moved into the basement, and relief provided where needed.

7. The term "taxpayer" is not clearly defined in our fire terminology. But for purposes of this discussion, it is a single building subdivided, generally by light partitions to accommodate two or more stores with a common cockloft. The term "supermarket" appears to have the same meaning throughout the country.

8. Taxpayers are built to burn and to collapse under fire conditions. They are of such inferior construction and so faulty from a fire protection viewpoint that, in many instances, the fire department cannot wage an effective attack. The cockloft space is a veritable lumberyard, except that the lumber is so arranged that it will burn faster in these occupanies than in lumber piles.

The taxpayer and supermarket fires in New York City were so numerous and devasting that a sprinkler program was developed whereby some chain supermarkets agreed to the installation of automatic sprinkler systems in a scheduled five-year period. The law in New York City granted the fire commissioner the discretionary power to order extinguishing systems to be installed where the hazard was severe. Conferences between supermarket representatives and fire department officials were extremely difficult at first, but through perseverance and compromise, a program was agreed upon and implemented.

Any taxpayer or supermarket with areas in excess of 10,000 square feet, or where there is inadequate means of ventilating the building, should be equipped with an automatic sprinkler system.

9. Collapse possibilities are so imminent that you cannot safely assign men to the roof or to positions inside the store.

Ceilings can come down without warning. In newer supermarkets, expansion of unprotected steel members may suddenly push out an exterior wall. The roof will fail and continue to fail throughout the fire. If a smoke explosion occurs under any kind of wind conditions, the flames will have a blast effect on any close leeward exposures. The commander must be wary, for the unpredictable is sure to occur. His principal job is to operate safely and yet prevent the extension of the fire to other buildings.

10. You have one chance of success in this fire. Unless all operations are closely coordinated, the fire fighting forces will have to be withdrawn.

Let us try to understand this situation. During the flame-production period, the highly heated products of combustion rise and mushroom throughout the hanging ceiling space. These gases are combustible and hot, but, since the oxygen is limited, the mixture is too rich to burn. Provide the oxygen, and the fire will roar.

Therefore, the key to success in this operation is to control the inflow of oxygen to the fire area and the ceiling space. The laddermen can cut the roof in any spot and they will see fire. An inference is then made that the fire is throughout the cockloft space. Actually, it is not. As the gases surge from a roof opening, they combine with the newly available oxygen and, naturally, the men witness fire. As the combustible gases flow out, air flows in. This provides the proper mixture to cause flaming combustion within this space. At the time you arrive at the scene, you have a distinct advantage, for the gases within the cockloft space are acting as a suppressant. Release these gases under the wrong conditions and you lose your advantage and perhaps your fire.

If the area at the street level is opened prematurely, the inflow of oxygen will cause flaming combustion wherever the oxygen combined with the highly heated gases.

*In Fighting This Fire:*
   (1) Call sufficient companies to give proper consideration to all the exposures.

(2) Stretch a minimum of two 2½-inch lines to the street front.

(3) Locate the heart of fire as may be determined by sense of touch on glass doors, windows, heat marks on roof, etc.

(4) Cut roof over the hottest area to make a large opening for ventilation. The opening should be commensurate with the building area. In opening up for ventilation, first cut roof boards to the full size of the opening to be made before removing any boards.

(5) Force entrance door to provide access to the seat of the fire. Then close the door until you are ready to move engine companies into the fire area.

(6) When the laddermen are ready to remove roof boards, open the skylights above the fire area. If no skylight is available, the ceiling must be pushed down as the roof boards are pulled.

(7) As soon as the roof boards are being removed, in conjunction with removal of the skylight, the engine company advances its line. If the area is large, have a second line ready to advance with first line.

(8) As the enginemen advance toward the hottest area, provide whatever horizontal ventilation is available in the direction toward which the enginemen are advancing.

(9) As the hose line sweeps the area, the generated steam will replace the combustible gases surging through the roof opening.

This close coordination of line advancement with ventilation will reduce temperature quickly. At this time, any other stores associated with this building can be enetered, ventilated, ceilings pulled and partitions examined. If you cut holes in the roof now, even in remote areas, you will discover that the wooden members are charred, indicating a process of destructive distillation. To be sure, they were cooking, but since they lacked oxygen, they were not flaming.

## DEFENSIVE STRATEGY—TEXTILE MILL FIRE (Figure 7)

The six-story heavy timber mill-constructed building was occupied originally as a textile mill, but at the time of the fire is in process of demolition. The fire doors to the elevator shaft are left open to facilitate demolition operations.

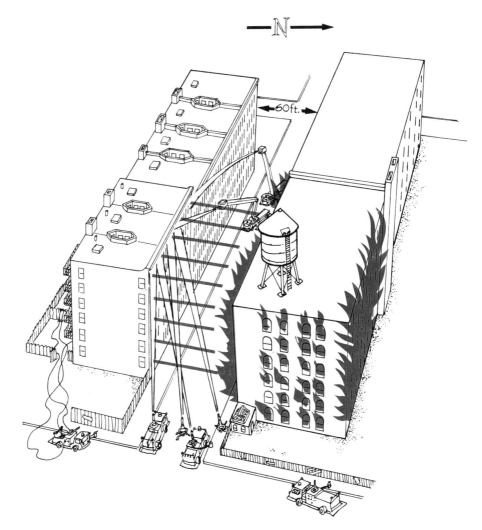

Figure 7. *This was an actual fire and the drawing does not exaggerate the condition.*

**CONSTRUCTION**

Construction consisted of brick exterior walls; cast iron columns, 6 feet on center, in the cellar and first floor; 12 x 12-inch wooden columns, 6 feet on center, on higher floors. Wooden beams 8 x 14 inches, approximately 25 feet long, were spaced 6 feet apart. Floors consisted of 4-inch wooden planking, 12 inches wide, which in turn were covered by ordinary 1 inch tongue and groove flooring. No concealed spaces were present in the design of the structure. Stairways were enclosed in brick walls and stairs were constructed entirely of metal. Large elevator shafts were located at the easterly side of each section of the mill. Fire doors were provided at all openings to stairs and elevator shafts.

*DIMENSIONS*

100 x 150 feet.

*WEATHER*

Mild and clear with a very light wind.

*ADJOINING BUILDING*

The mill consisted of two sections, independent of each other. Each section was approximately 100 x 150 feet and was separated from the other by a fire wall with openings protected by fire doors. Fortunately, at the time of the fire these fire doors are still existent and most of them are closed.

*FIRE DEVELOPMENT*

The fire originated in the cellar and extended up the unprotected elevator shaft. Upon arrival of the first-alarm companies, the fire has seriously involved the cellar and first and second floors of the east building. Within five minutes, the fire has complete possession of the entire six floors.

*COLLAPSE*

Within 25 to 30 minutes of arrival of fire units, the north, south and east walls completely collapsed. The presence of a large metal water tank 20 feet above the roof was largely responsible for the early collapse of the building. The metal tank supports were quickly weakened by the fire and permitted the tank to crash through the roof to the cellar.

### EXPOSED TENEMENTS

The street is 60 feet wide. Five and six-story, old-type, occupied tenements are south of the fire building.

### QUESTIONS

*1. What is the strategic factor presented by this fire and what type of strategy should be pursued?*

*2. There is some fire extension to the adjoining companion mill building, since a few of the fire doors were left open. The companies operating in this building reported that they had little trouble extinguishing the fires and no problem with smoke. Why?*

3. *What deviation from true mill construction probably contributed substantially to the collapse of this structure?*

4. *Discuss mill construction from the following viewpoints:*
   A. Absence of concealed spaces.
   B. Slow burning characteristics of its structural members.
   C. Structural stability.

5. *The collapse originated at the roof level with the failure of the water tank supports. The roof and each subsequent floor added to the weight and stresses on the columns below. With column failure, this collapse was total and instantaneous. What conditions can you anticipate when this massive weight impacts at street level?*

6. *If the front wall collapsed outwardly and the floors temporarily remained intact, would the fire problems be greater or less than in total collapse? Give reasons.*

7. *Presume there is a row of one and two-story buildings on the east side and close to the fire building. The roofs of these buildings should not be used as vantage points for positioning heavy stream appliances, and companies should not be assigned to the inside of these structures except for quick survey and evacuation purposes. Give reasons.*

8. *The spread of fire throughout the building was unusually rapid, since compartmentation had been negated by demolition procedures. The collapse occurred about 25 to 30 minutes after the arrival of first alarm units. Presume that within the first 15 minutes of operations, one elevating platform or ladder pipe stream, three ladder pipes and five deluge sets were operational. All of these streams were positioned in the rear of the fire building, some streams penetrating the window openings of the upper floors and a*

*few of the streams washing the facing of the building. What is*
*your evaluation of these procedures?*

1. In this case, the strategic factor is the enormous body of fire
   which is radiating intense heat across the 60 foot-wide street
   toward the row of tenements. This compelling factor dictates
   the pursuit of a defensive plan intended to protect people in
   the tenements as well as the tenements, themselves. Extension of the fire to the closely-built tenements will result in a
   conflagration situation.

   Heavy exterior streams must be activated quickly to cover
   the fronts of the exposed structures. Any inclination to use a
   water curtain on the front of the fire building will be
   ineffective in controlling radiant heat and should therefore be
   avoided. Engine and ladder company personnel will have to
   enter the tenements from the rear to evacuate occupants and
   bring in hand lines from the next street. After extinguishing
   fires in the tenements, these lines should be siamesed to
   develop heavy exterior streams for heat wave control. Reliance on the streams operating from the street will be thereby
   reduced.

   Because of the collapse possibility at fires of this magnitude,
   personnel and equipment should be positioned with extreme
   care in the street surrounding the fire building. Rubble from
   the collapsing walls can be projected horizontally as far as 200
   feet.

2. This fire has some of the characteristics of a fire storm. The absence of a ground wind accelerated a near-perfect vertical updraft. A column of hot air and burning gases rising vertically will draw air in at the sides. The post-fire critique disclosed that greater alarm units operating in the west section of the mill observed wind currents being carried from the exposed section into the fire building through openings in the party fire wall. The entrance of fresh air intensified the fire. Also, this phenomenon minimized extension possibilities in the west section and permitted operation of streams from the west exposure.

3. The unprotected cast-iron columns in the cellar and first floor would have lost a great deal of their compressive strength because of absorption of heat from this massive fire. The crushing load of the tank caused their collapse and, in turn, the collapse of the entire structure. Without tank and column failure, a true mill-constructed building could have withstood the ravages of this fire for a much longer period of time.

4. A. Concealed spaces within structures complicate the business of fire attack. They make for stubborn, persistent and hard-to-fight fires. Therefore the absence of concealed spaces is of great advantage in fighting fires in mill construction.

   B. Heavy timber construction, by virtue of the size and mass of planks and timbers provides a slow burning building. Since the ratio of the exposed surfaces to the total volume of these combustible members is small, and since heat conduction through them is relatively slow, failure under heat and flame attack is retarded. When the exposed wood surfaces char in a fire, the insulation effect of the charred wood further retards heat penetration.

   C. For a building to qualify as heavy timber construction, the columns cannot be less than 8 inches in any dimension, and wood beams and girders cannot be less than 6 inches wide nor less than 10 inches in depth. With this type of framing, structural failure occurs only under the most extreme fire conditions.

5. With the floors collapsing one upon the other in quick succession, the air and fire will be compressed and forced out toward the exposures. Tremendous sheets of flame will accompany the heat blasted into the street and scorch anything in its path. This is the time of maximum heat radiation, since the fire is no longer partially enclosed by walls. The radiation hazard changes from an area source to a line source. This is advantageous, since the radiation hazard will now diminish inversely with the distance. (For further explanation of radiant heat transmission refer to Chapter 5 under caption "Distance.")

After the initial burst of radiant heat at the time of the collapse, the situation levels off and the problems start to diminish. With the floors collapsing upon each other, the compression of the massive accumulation of building material debris at the cellar and first floor levels will extinguish most of the fire.

6. The radiation problem would be greatly magnified. With the front wall intact, radiation is emitted through the window openings. The area of windows compared to the area of the wall is relatively small. The wall is the principal shield from radiation. Remove the wall and the radiation problem is greatly magnified.

In addition, you still have six floors of fire to contend with plus the area factor. Further, the intensity of fire will increase since the inflow of oxygen will be greater. On the other hand with total collapse, the level of radiation increases instantaneously but diminishes rapidly since the impact of the falling building materials substantially reduces the fire. This fire is now within easy reach of streams and will be quickly extinguished.

7. It is very hard to predict the time and the nature of collapse. With six floors fully involved and the fire burning with such fury, you can be certain that the walls will collapse. The walls may go outward or inward, depending on so many factors that computations cannot be made at the fire scene. With column failures, the principle impact would be in a downward

direction. The walls of the textile mill are 100 feet high. The danger area is at least 200 feet from fire building. It is much farther than some textbooks indicate. Therefore, personnel could not be permitted on the roofs of the one and two-story buildings, and you cannot unnecessarily jeopardize firemen within these buildings since the weight and energy of the falling side walls could readily cause roof failure in these buildings.

8. First, it would be too dangerous to position these units in the rear and in close proximity to the fire building. Nevertheless, this battery of streams would have little apparent effect upon the fire. You would have to mass sufficient streams to absorb the generated heat. The science of measuring heat production at fire situations has not been advanced to a degree whereby the fire chief can establish the amount of water needed for each particular fire. Therefore, we must work from our experiences.

In W.N.Y.F., 4th issue of 1970, a report is made on a fire in a vacant factory building, five stories high, 75 x 75 feet in area. All five floors of the building were fully involved and all streams specified in this question were in operation with no apparent effect. The companies were withdrawn, a secondary line of defense was established and shortly thereafter the building collapsed. It is interesting to note that in this article they state that brands ignited a building 200 feet northwest of the fire building, and a church approximately 150 feet from the fire building required two $2^1/_2$-inch lines. The fire building was only five stores high and the debris of collapse landed as much as 140 feet from the fire building.

In moving the streams from window to window, some of the water will be washing the wall facings. The cooling effect on the exterior walls will cause contraction of the wall while the fire is heating the interior walls and causing expansion. This will also contribute to the collapse of the structure.

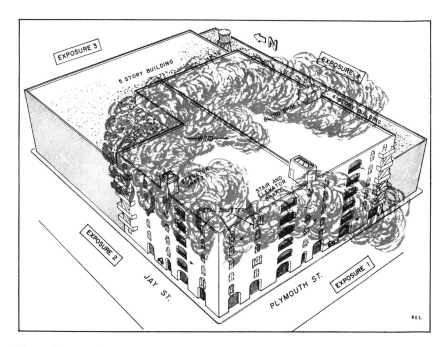

Figure 8. *Combustible stock, high piling and a large area were insurmounta-ble to fire forces. Exterior streams could not adequately cool the massive fire to allow interior attack.*

## STRATEGY MODIFICATIONS—PEERLESS WAREHOUSE FIRE (Figure 8)

There were two distinct buildings of similar construction with fire wall separation. Since some of the fire doors were open on the fourth, fifth and sixth floors and fire had spread through these openings in major proportions before the arrival of any fire companies, therefore, the fire building was actually the aggregate area of both buildings. The standpipe systems of both buildings were used by the fire forces.

*CONSTRUCTION*

Walls were 20 inches of brickwork; floors were 4-inch thick tongue and groove boards covered with a 1½-inch wearing surface of wood; beams were 12 x 18 inches, 6 feet on center;

girders were double 12 x 18 inch wood timber, standing on edge, bolted and placed 19 feet apart. The girders were supported by columns of quadruple 12 x 12-inch wood timbers joined to form a 24-inch square column and placed at 12 foot intervals. The roof was fashioned of 4½-inch wood planks, covered successively with 4 inches of terracotta tile and 2 inches of cement, tarpaper and gravel.

### DIMENSIONS

Irregular, 300 x 300 feet and six stories high.

### OCCUPANCY

The buildings served as a warehouse for furniture, food freezers, refrigerators, washing machines, dryers, pianos, toys and chinaware. The fire load was extremely severe.

### NORTH EXPOSURE

A five-story building continuously abutted the fire building on the north. There were no openings in the abutting walls.

### EAST EXPOSURE

A four-story sprinklered warehouse was on the east. The adjoining walls of the fire building and this exposure were unpierced for the full line of contact.

### QUESTIONS

*1. What is the strategic factor at this fire?*

2. *The companies successfully penetrated the fourth floor and were able to direct streams from the horizontal opening in the fire wall toward the Jay Street side of the building. While these companies were fighting for control of the fourth floor, what immediate tactics should be initiated in respect to the fifth and sixth floors?*

3. *Ladder pipes were positioned so their nozzles could be placed within the windows of the fifth and sixth floors. Ten ladder pipes were in operation at this time. But the high piling and density of stock limited outside stream penetration and prevented major absorption of the high heat. The fire conditions grew worse rather than better. Companies attempting to move in on the fifth floor from the fire-protected stairway were challenged by a more severe heat situation than on the fourth floor. At this time, the sixth floor was untenable. What was the vital factor that made it imperative to change from offensive to defensive operations?*

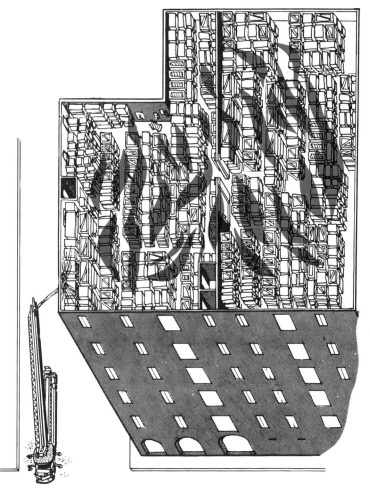

Figure 9. *This illustration shows the ineffectiveness of the exterior streams. The stream immediately encounters high piling and penetrates 5-10 feet.*

*4. The closed fire shutters on Jay and Plymouth Sts. were a significant disadvantage in this situation. Why?*

5. *The roof was fashioned of 4¹/₂-inch wood planks, covered successively with 4 inches of terra cotta tile, and 2 inches of cement, tar paper and gravel. This superior type construction proved a distinct disadvantage at this fire. Why?*

6. *There was great evidence of a pressure buildup on the fifth and sixth floors, resulting in grave concern that a smoke explosion would occur. To relieve this condition, two companies under the supervision of a chief officer were ordered to the roof with power tools to relieve the pent up gases through direct roof ventilation. What was the justification for taking this action at this stage of the fire?*

7. *No type of building can indefinitely survive an inferno of this magnitude. Once the roof had been opened to relieve the pent-up gases, there were no other outward manifestations indicating collapse. But since the exterior streams had only a negligible effect on the fire, eventual collapse had to be anticipated. For this reason, a secondary line of defense was*

*established. What are the procedures in establishing a secondary line of defense?*

1. The strategic factor is the construction of the building. This type of building has structural integrity. It is designed and constructed to withstand the ravages of fire. If the construction was brick-joist, the strategy would have been defensive. It is safe to attempt an interior offensive attack.

2. To restrain the spread and the intensity of the fire while hand lines are being stretched, and during their early operation on the fourth floor, large exterior streams should be directed into the fifth and sixth floors from both the Jay Street and Plymouth Street sides of the building. The area of this building is 300 x 300 feet. The fire loading is severe, and the spread of the fire has been rapid. Under these conditions the offensive attack is in jeopardy. Allow the entire area to become engulfed in flames on the three floors, and the heat generation would drive the companies off the floor. Therefore, heavy streams from the exterior must be used to keep the fire within the range of interior hand lines.

3. The critical factor which made it imperative to change from offensive to defensive operations was the unusual size of the fire area. The fire continued to grow larger and larger. The building code governing the construction of this building limited the dimensions to 150 x 150 feet. The fire wall with the automatic self-closing devices was intended to restrict the

spread of fire to one building. If the fire wall integrity had been maintained, the fire probably would have been controlled. The fire-protected stairway provided a good bridgehead for interior operations; there were a number of window openings on Jay Street and Plymouth Street for limited ladder pipe penetration. The fire escapes provided additional access for engine companies to the upper floors. The rear wall of the sixth floor could readily have been breached. Then the fire doors could have been opened when lines were in position. There was some roof ventilation through a skylight. If the fire suppression was satisfactory, companies with pneumatic drills would have resorted to breaching the roof. However, with a fire area of 300 x 300 feet, the ballgame was entirely different. The problems continued to multiply, the area and temperature of the fire rapidly increased under these conditions, and the streams lacked efficacy.

Since automatic or self-closing devices in fire walls may fail to function, an automatic sprinkler system should be mandatory in such large area buildings even when the construction is of a superior type. With an area of 150 x 150 feet with some access to the fire area from four sides, fire operations can generally be successful. Double the fire area, and under major fire conditions, fire operations generally will be unsuccessful.

4. 80% of the shutters were in the closed position. The fire was on three floors on arrival, and jumping out of the unprotected windows on both Jay and Plymouth Sts. The aerials were readied for ladder pipe operations. Opening shutters from aerial ladders is always precarious and slow. The closed shutters prohibited rapid offensive operations, since ventilation originally was very limited. The shutters also impeded exterior stream operations. With elevating platforms, there would have been much greater success in safe removal of shutters. However, this type of equipment was not in service at the time of this fire. Wire glass windows are a much more practical solution to window protection than metal shutters.

5. The amount of ventilation provided by skylight and bulkhead openings generally is inadequate at major fire situations. Therefore, the roof must be further opened. With the fire

raging on three floors of a large area building, commitment of ladder personnel to roof operations is precarious. Under these conditions, no commander can predict precisely what is going to happen. He must be extremely careful not to unnecessarily jeopardize his firefighters. With the ordinary type of roof construction, the fire would have burned through the roof, thus venting itself.

6. The action to vent the roof was a calculated risk because these members could have been trapped by failure of the roof. However, the smoke explosion could have resulted in a complete collapse of the building or a portion thereof, endangering fire personnel and other people in the area. Although fire chiefs are governed by the principle of not unnecessarily jeopardizing the lives of firefighters to save property, this risk was taken since many lives would have been in jeopardy if the smoke explosion had materialized.

7. The following procedures were established at this actual situation.
   A. Companies continued to operate exterior streams from street positions and the roofs of exposures, since collapse was not imminent.
   B. Additional companies and personnel were called to the fire scene.
   C. The standpipe systems in the warehouses across Jay and Plymouth Streets were fed by two pumpers for each of the buildings. The pumpers operated at 200 psi. Both $2^1/_2$ and 3-inch lines fed deluge sets.
   D. Three-inch lines with playpipes were stretched up the interior stairs to the upper floors.
   E. A battery of high pressure streams was positioned on the upper floors and roofs of these buildings. Operating in this manner, they easily traversed the 60 and 80-foot-wide streets, deluging the fire building.
   F. Ladder pipe and other streams operating on the street were then shut down. The apparatus, hose and other equipment were removed from streets around the fire building.
   G. Police then barricaded the street and no civilians or fire

personnel were permitted within the barricaded area. Two chief officers were designated safety officers to enforce the safety procedures.

### CONCLUSION

The major collapse occurred about 24 hours after the start of operations. The wall on Plymouth St. hinged at the top of the third floor and fell as a monolithic unit, striking the building opposite for its entire height. This was followed in a split second by the front wall on Jay Street. This, too, hinged at the top of the third floor and fell as a monolithic unit. The top struck the building opposite about halfway between the first and second floors. There were no personal injuries.

# Chapter 3

# Reconnaissance and the Fire Situation

**FURNITURE WAREHOUSE FIRE (Figure 1)**

A furniture warehouse has unprotected steel framing with a flat, unpierced, steel, insulated roof. The non-bearing concrete

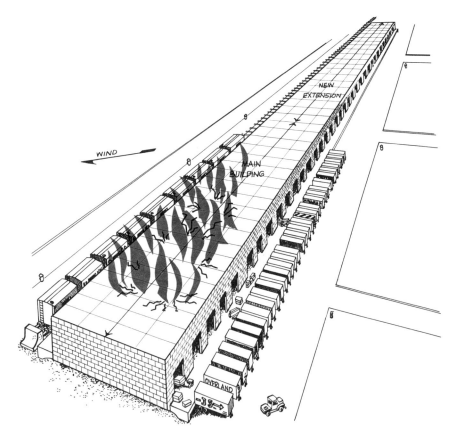

Figure 1. *Do you attack the fire or use your limited resources to prevent involvement of the new extension?*

70

block walls have many large overhead doors to accommodate the loading and unloading of trailer trucks and railroad box cars.

The building is 152 x 652 feet, but a nearly completed addition has added 600 more feet to the building. The east wall of the original building has been removed, so that the entire area is open and undivided.

The floor is a concrete slab laid directly on the ground, and the roof is about 12 feet above the floor. There is a loading platform about four feet high on the north and south sides of the building.

*OCCUPANCY*

The fire loading is severe, consisting primarily of furniture of all types. In many areas, the furniture is piled to the underside of the ceiling. However, the aisle space is good, with a 10-foot aisle running the length of the building and with many 6-foot cross aisles.

*FIRE PROTECTION*

There are 2½ gallon extinguishers throughout the building, spaced about 100 feet apart.

*WEATHER*

It is a clear day, with a temperature of about 40 degrees. There is a moderately strong wind of approximately 15–20 mph from the southeast.

*ACCESS TO FIRE*

On the north side is a railroad siding and box cars are at all of the door openings, either loading or unloading furniture. The box cars are within a foot of the building, and cannot be moved immediately. There are 33 trailer trucks backed into the many door openings on the south side of the building. There are no tractors hitched to any of the trailers.

*FIRE*

Fire started about 11 a.m. It was fought for 15 minutes by employees using hand extinguishers. It originated in about the center of the original building. When the first apparatus arrived, flames were seen above the roof at the center portion of the building. All the cargo doors were open, so the firemen had clear visibility of a large mass of fire in the center portion.

*RESPONSE*

Three engine companies responded, but the water system was limited to about 2000 gpm. A 100-foot aerial with a ladder pipe also responded. There were at least 50 paid and volunteer firemen at the scene.

*EXPOSURES*

The exposures were limited to the trailers, box cars and new addition.

*QUESTIONS*

*1. What effect do the following factors have on developing the strategy and tactics for coping with this fire situation?*
   A. Extent of fire
   B. Construction features
   C. Time of day
   D. Wind
   E. Water supply

2. *What consideration must be given to life hazard at the fire situation?*

3. *A size-up is a fact-finding phase of managing a fire. Discuss size-up in respect to any major situation.*

1. **Factors Influencing Strategy and Tactics**

*Extent of Fire*—Flames showing through the insulated steel roof deck indicate that the steel is buckling and the seams are tearing apart, allowing massive flame to escape. This is a major fire on arrival and its centralized location eliminates any hope of confining the fire to a limited portion of the building.

*Constructional Features*—Unprotected steel frame construction with an unpierced steel roof deck is prone to early collapse under heavy fire conditions and severe fire loading. Steel at temperatures of 1000–1600° F rapidly loses its tensile strength. In fact, at 1600° F., structural steel will have lost more than 90 percent of its tensile strength.

Steel expands 8 parts in a million for each degree of rise in temperature. When heated to 1000° F, a 100-foot length of steel will expand about 9 inches and at 1600° F, the expansion will be about 15 inches. Such expansion may push out exterior walls and certainly the steel will buckle and fail.

*Time of Day*—Because it is daytime, the truck and railroad siding doors are open. This will considerably intensify the fire since the oxygen supply is continuous.

*Wind*—The wind is brisk, and blowing in the direction of the railroad siding and box cars. Since the box cars are so close to the building, the convection and radiant heat will make operations in this area hazardous and untenable. The closeness of the cars precludes any safe refuge or retreat for the fire fighting forces.

However, the wind is favorable for operations on the south side of the building and the 33 trailer trucks may be salvageable.

The direction of the wind may make it feasible to close the overhead doors on the south side of the building to reduce the draft of the fire. This would have to be done in the early stages of the fire and only if the doors were easily operable. The wind will blow the fire from the south to the north side of the building. Because there is no fire loading within the new addition, the probability of success within this area is greatly improved.

*Water Supply*—The judicious use of water is the key to success in this operation.

The expenditure of the available 2000 gpm through the use of master streams or ladder pipes directed at the original fire will be useless and will result in the loss of both buildings and both loading sides of the building. Streams directed through the door openings will not penetrate through the high piled stock. Streams directed over the roof will be ineffective as the insulated steel roof covering will separate, fall onto the stock, cover portions of the burning material and resist extinguishment for a prolonged period. Attempts to save the railroad side in the face of the wind and early direction of the fire will be a severe waste of valuable and limited fire flow. Use of large solid streams directed from the new building toward the heat of the fire will also be wasted. The length and width of the building combined with heavy fire loading, high piling, and low ceiling will prevent adequate penetration.

There are three exposures in this fire situation:
(1) The new building addition
(2) The trailer trucks and their contents
(3) The railroad cars and their contents.

Since the water supply is limited to 2000 gpm, this precludes covering all positions effectively. The commander must make a decision of priority, which is always the essence of strategy development.

The newly constructed addition to the building has no fire loading and will be destroyed only if heat is allowed to spread in its direction and twist its structural members. The wind direction is favorable to accompishing this objective. Two master stream fog nozzles, one from each side of the new building, will be likely to control the fire spread in this direction and will expend approximately 1500 gallons of water per minute.

These fog streams will not extinguish the main fire, but can keep the structural steel cool and prevent some of the radiant heat traveling along the upper portions of the newly erected unprotected steel. The fog streams will be principally directed to the upper regions of the new building and intermitently toward the older building to control fire spread in the area proximate to the new extension. It may also be feasible to use power saws with special blades to cut a trench across the new roof to ventilate smoke and heat.

There are still approximately 500 gpm of water available. The wind direction dictates operating on the south side of the building. About five $1\frac{1}{2}$-inch lines can be stretched to protect the trailer trucks and their contents. Certainly some tractors must be at the scene, and under the protection of the $1\frac{1}{2}$-inch lines, some trailers can be moved to safe locations, where the $1\frac{1}{2}$-inch lines can be used to extinguish any fire.

When later arriving equipment becomes available in the form of mutual aid or distance units, the chief officer must continue to control his water supply rigidly. Any further connection to hydrants in the immediate vicinity will steal his present supply. Pumpers must be connected to distant large mains or to drafting positions and relays must be arranged to reduce friction loss. It must also be remembered that water being drafted from polluted supplies should not be interconnected with lines or pumpers connected to the domestic potable water supply.

**2. Life Hazard**

The chief's first concern will be life hazard. Through rapid consultation with management at the scene, the commander must assure himself that it is reasonably certain that all employees are out of the premises and he must direct that no employee attempt any act without his direct permission. If a fast rescue must be made, he must weigh its potential. He would be justified in assigning whatever forces are required to effect such removal in the shortest possible time.

A very important aspect of life hazard concerns the fire fighting force. Since the collapse of the building is predictable, interior attack would unnecessarily jeopardize the members of the fire fighting units. Also, no member should be allowed on the roof of the fire building. Since the walls may be pushed out by the expansion of the steel members; great caution must be exercised in positioning units. Since there is no quick means of escape on the north side of the building because of the closeness of the box cars to the exterior walls, no operation should be permitted in this area. On the south wall, firemen may be permitted, at the time of arrival, to attempt to close the overhead doors, but only if the conditions indicate this can be done safely.

**3. Size-Up of Fire Situation**

A skillful size-up of a fire provides the basis for a plan of action. It corresponds to the military "estimate of the situation." In essence, it should answer these questions; What and where are the problems? Which problems require primary consideration? Is there a particular situation of extreme urgency?

Each officer who will command the fire should, on his arrival, make an independent size-up, and this should include consideration of actions already taken, the existing strategy, and the strength and disposition of forces. The emphasis is on the word "independent" since conditions may have changed since the previous size-up or the previous size-up may be faulty or misleading.

The newly promoted chief officer must consciously force himself to make a size-up and to estimate the importance or weight of each factor. His size-up may be of little value until experience, gained at many fires, tells him what to look for, what is important and how to get reliable information. Experience will also teach him that things often look different than they really are. He will learn that aggressive, effective operations may change the picture in a few minutes and that many peripheral problems will be solved by the "main action" without the need to deploy large forces for these purposes. This latter point relates to the concept of "economy of forces" or the concentration of efforts on major problems.

The experienced chief officer can make a size-up with considerable speed and accuracy. He has developed skill in making visual surveys of conditions, in sensing the true nature of a situation, in asking sharp, pertinent questions and in seeking information on key points. He uses his time effectively and assembles many of his points while responding, leaving fewer to be checked on arrival.

What are the essential features or factors in a size-up? About 14 or 15 points are generally cited. The chief must assemble his information, bit by bit, as it becomes available. When important facts or data are missing, he must persistently seek to obtain this information at the earliest possible moment. Information at major fires may be difficult to obtain or the transmission of information may be delayed or overlooked. This must be anticipated and overcome by establishing the necessary communications systems at the scene. It is axiomatic that accurate, timely communications are imperative for effective operations and become more important and more critical as the scope of operations increases. To operate without adequate information is to operate blindly and haphazardly.

Certain factors can be ascertained or estimated while responding to the fire:
(1) Time
(2) Wind force and direction
(3) Snow, ice, rain
(4) Depleted response and depleted manpower
(5) General traffic conditions
(6) Water supplies—in broad aspects
(7) Capabilities of officers at the fire

Other factors are immediately observable upon arrival:
(1) Height of buildings
(2) Frontage of fire building
(3) General occupancy type—tenement, factory, school, etc.
(4) Construction type—Frame, NFP or FP
(5) Nature of exposures—on sides 1, 2, and 4
(6) Siameses and fire escapes—at front and perhaps sides
(7) Floors apparently involved
(8) Accessibility

The assimilation of this data while responding or immediately upon arrival gives the commander more time to concentrate on obtaining other essential information. By questioning the previous commander and sector chiefs, and if necessary ladder company officers, the size-up can be essentially completed. The information sought would be:
(1) Actual extent of fire—size of fire area, floors involved
(2) Depth of fire building
(3) Unusual floor layout
(4) Exposures at rear or not visible from front
(5) Openings to adjoining buildings
(6) Location and involvement of shafts
(7) Unusually hazardous occupancies
(8) What is burning?—actual occupancies of fire floors
(9) Positions of companies and chief officers.

Certain matters are of such significance that they should be *rechecked* even though they should have been ascertained and reported during the early phases of operations:
(1) Has the building been searched or evacuated?
(2) Has the roof been properly vented?

(3) Are there dangerous roof structures—large signs, tanks, etc?

(4) Are there unusually good roof venting facilities?

(5) Is there a rear fire escape or a second stairway?

(6) Are sprinklers and standpipes being properly used?

(7) Are closed iron shutters hampering advance?

(8) Are there indications of marked structural weakness?

(9) Are there good stairway enclosures?

(10) Are lines advancing? If not, what is the reason?

The size-up factors were very useful to the author. They increased his knowledge, but they were not formulated in such a manner that the factors alone could guide him through a logical plan of action. So throughout the years he transposed this knowledge into an operational plan which provided a sequence to logically guide him in the movements of managing a fire situation.

**OPERATION PLAN FOR COMMANDING A COMPLEX FIRE SITUATION**

I. Planning

  A. *Get facts*

    1. Fire situation

      (a) Location of fire—what is burning?

      (b) Extent of fire

      (c) Life hazard problems

      (d) Exposure problems

      (e) Confinement problems

      (f) Extinguishment problems

    2. Building situation—for each building endangered

      (a) Height and area

      (b) Construction

      (c) Occupancies

      (d) Layout

      (e) Fire Protection facilities

      (f) Special hazards

    3. Outside situation

      (a) Weather

(b) Time

(c) Water Supply

(d) Street conditions

4. Tactics

   (a) Outside streams

   (b) Companies assigned to fire building

   (c) Companies assigned exposures 1, 2, 3, 4

   (d) Companies standing by

   (e) Position of chief officers

5. Communications

   (a) A field communications unit should respond to all major fires. Generally the command post is established near this unit.

   (b) There are three distinct radio channels for communications at fire scenes. The field communications unit is in contact with headquarters. A walkie-talkie channel maintains communications between the chief of department and his sector commanders. A walkie-talkie channel establishes communications between companies and battalion chiefs.

6. Other helpful agencies

   (a) Police

   (b) Utility companies

   (c) Water department

   (d) Engineer or other person in charge of plant or facility.

B. *Appraisal of facts*

1. By observation

2. Inspection where necessary

3. Walkie-talkie contacts

C. *Decisions*

1. Determine the strategic factors

2. What additional measures are necessary to protect life

3. What are the imminent conditions requiring immediate action?

4. What fire strategy should be employed:

   (a) Offensive

   (b) Offensive—Defensive

   (c) Defensive—Offensive

      (d) Defensive

      (e) Indirect Method of Attack

    5. Men and Machines

      (a) What apparatus, special units and manpower will be necessary?

II. Organization and Staffing (Figures 2 and 3)

  A. *Area command*

    1. Placed a chief officer in charge of designated fire areas, such as:

      (a) Exposure 1

      (b) Exposure 2

      (c) Exposure 3

      (d) Exposure 4

      (e) Fire Building—5

      (f) Remote but serious exposures

  B. *Communications*

    1. Each sector chief apprised of conditions, the strategy of attack and the companies assigned to his command.

    2. Each sector chief will, at five-minute intervals establish walkie-talkie contact and provide information, as to:

      (a) Changing conditions—favorable or unfavorable

      (b) Immediate needs

      (c) Probable needs

    3. When facts have been assimilated, take action in accordance with situation.

  C. *Chain of Command and Unity of Command*

    1. Commander at the fire will transmit orders to and receive information from the sector commanders.

    2. Each sector commander will establish liaison with each officer assigned to his sector and establish the manner of flow of orders and transmission of information.

    3. Companies will operate only on orders flowing through chain of command.

III. Controls

      (a) A control point must be established

      (b) Sanborn and water maps are an integral part of the control system

      (c) In complex buildings, headquarters can provide

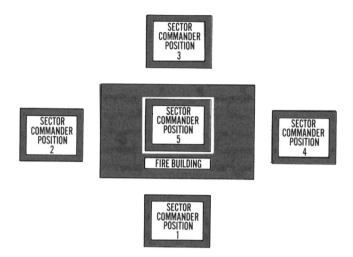

Figure 2.   *Sector commanders.*

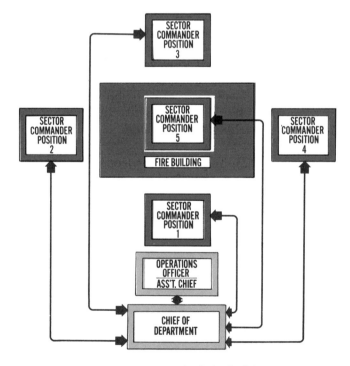

Figure 3.   *Span of control of chief of department.*

pertinent information beyond that which is contained on a Sanborn map

There must be constant observation and investigation of conditions that appear to be at variance with reported information. Method of control will essentially evolve about:

(a) A clear delegation of authority
(b) Following chain of command
(c) Each superior holding his immediate subordinate accountable for results.

D. *Span of control of chief of Department*

It was the practice in New York City that all companies would report directly to the chief of department for orders. With 20, 25 or 30 companies reporting directly to the chief of department at major alarms, it soon became evident to the author that most of his time was consumed in talking with company officers. Studies in management have shown that the higher the level at which you operate and the more complex the situation, the narrower the span of control should be. Managing a fire is no different in principle then managing a fire department or any other large organization. The same principles prevail.

To shorten the span of control of the chief of department, it seemed feasible to make the next Chief-in-command the operations officer. His position at the fire was immediately in front of the chief of department. All company officers, battalion chiefs and those deputy chiefs not designated sector commanders reported to and received orders from the operation officer, who was constantly in verbal communication with the chief of department, who kept him informed of the strategy and tactical procedures he was to use. The operations officer assigns officers and units to sector commanders.

Now the chain of command of the chief of department consisted of 5 sector commanders and 1 operation officer. The chief of department was in constant communication with these officers. They were feeding him information on all espects of the fire. The chief had more sources of information than anyone else at the scene. His estimate of the situation had the greatest scope. He who knows the most, can command the best.

*Chapter 4*

# *Building Construction and its Relation to Fire Strategy*

**Principal objective:**

To show the strong correlation between knowledge of constructional details and development of fire strategy.

## MULTIPLE RESIDENCE FIRE (Figures 1 and 2)

The 25 x 60-foot building is of brick joist construction, four stories high. The side walls are unpierced, and the party walls extend two feet above the roof. The cornice is firestopped at parapet walls. The stairway is open and structural members are principally of wood. There is a 40-foot rear yard.

*OCCUPANCY*

The building is residential. There is no secondary means of egress and the sprinkler installation is out of service.

84

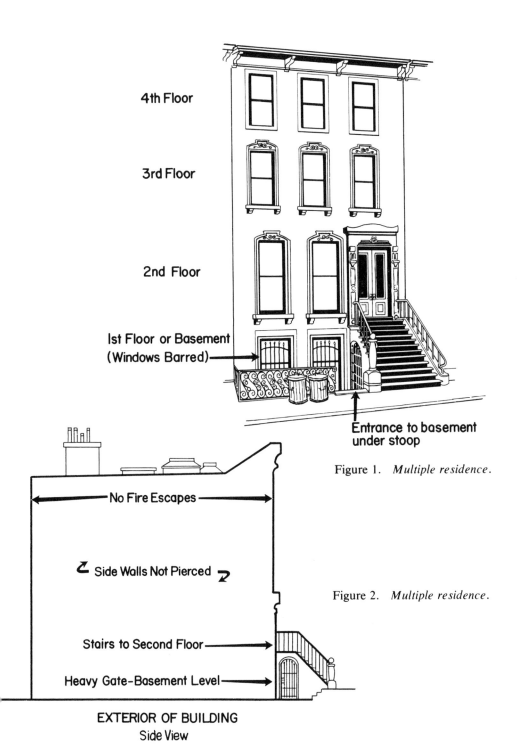

4th Floor

3rd Floor

2nd Floor

1st Floor or Basement
(Windows Barred)

Entrance to basement
under stoop

Figure 1. *Multiple residence.*

No Fire Escapes

Side Walls Not Pierced

Figure 2. *Multiple residence.*

Stairs to Second Floor

Heavy Gate-Basement Level

EXTERIOR OF BUILDING
Side View

Similar buildings exist on both sides.

Fire originates on the second floor in the stairway and extends up the open stairway to the upper two floors. The second, third and fourth floor rear rooms are all in flames. In fact, the fire is blowing 20-feet out of the fourth floor rear windows.

Three engines and two aerial ladder companies, with five men each, responded to the scene.

*1. The firemen, officers, and chief officers operating at this substantial fire go about their work in a most professional manner. There is no shouting and very little confusion. The fire is roaring up the stairway, blowing out of the rear of the building; smoke is enveloping the area, and the life hazard is serious. Yet the situation does not spark fear in the hearts of the firefighters. Why?*

2. This fire can invariably be handled with three engine company streams. The commanding officer generally will not transmit a second alarm Why?

3. The first engine company stretched a line up the interior stairs and advanced to the third floor. The second engine company stretched a line up the interior stairs to the second floor. What are the intended purposes of this second line?

4. Engine Companies 1 and 2 are assigned to the interior stairway and to control the fire on the second and third floors. What assignments would you give to Engine Company 3? Give reasons.

5. *At these fire situations, it is usual for one of the ladder companies to raise its aerial to the top floor, and for the other ladder company to raise its aerial to the roof. Two firemen with a roof rope and life belts climb the aerial and rescue any trapped tenants at rear of building. Justify this method.*

6. *Command at This Fire and Other First Alarm Operations*

   *The first arriving officer is in command until the arrival of a superior officer. While he is in command, his authority is absolute, and has parity with the authority of a chief of department. This principle is fairly well established throughout the country. Controversy arises as to where the battalion chief should position himself at first alarm operations. Some authors advocate that he stay at the street level and be visible to future arriving companies. Others recommend a position within the fire building. Discuss.*

7. *What is the strategic factor at this fire?*

1. Knowledge brings confidence. The company personnel have frequently inspected this type of building under the supervision of their company officers. The battalion and deputy chiefs spot-check these inspections. With this building inspection knowledge and the experience of putting out a number of similar fires, the personnel know that within 10 to 15 minutes, the fire will be under control. However, if these knowledgeable firefighters were special-called into the downtown commercial loft section to extinguish the same size fire, they may not be very effective. They can, in a reasonable period of time, become just as proficient at loft fires as they are in multiple residences, but to attain efficiency, any fire company will have to frequently inspect the loft buildings and become thoroughly acquainted with their particular construction and occupancy features.

*Know Your Buildings*—Your firefighting expertise is very much related to your knowledge of the construction of the buildings in your district, community or city. This knowledge comes from frequent inspections, diligent study of the pertinent building laws and relating this information to firefighting operations. As former Chief Gordon Vickery of the Seattle Fire Department so aptly put it, "Get off your butts and inspect."

2. The commander, by virtue of his building inspection activities, knows that:

   A. Rear exposure is a minimum of 40-feet away, and if there are similar buildings on street in the rear, the distance then becomes 80 feet. Therefore, the rear exposure problem is minimal.

   B. With the side bearing walls unpierced and extending two feet through the roof, and with the roof cornices fire-stopped, the probability is that there will be no extension to the adjoining buildings. If there is extension because of building defects, it probably will not be on a major scale.

   C. Since no exposures have to be initially covered, there is an engine company for each of the involved floors. Since the area of the building is small, there are windows front and rear for ventilation, and there is access to the fire

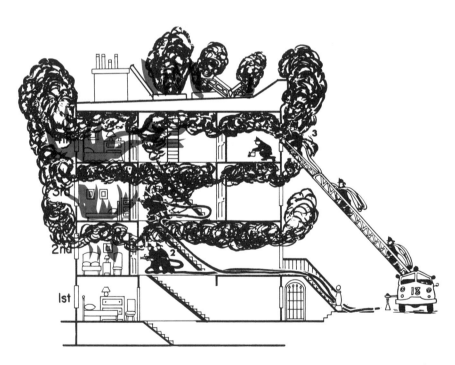

Figure 3.   *Stairway fire has been extinguished on 2nd and 3rd floors. Fire has been darkened on 2nd floor, and Engine 1 is about to extinguish fire on 3rd floor. Engine 3 will rapidly advance to rear of 4th floor since adequate rear and roof ventilation have been provided.*

through the interior stairway and aerial ladder. These fires are generally extinguished within 10 to 15 minutes with three engine streams.

3. The intended purposes of the second line are:
   A. To complete extinguishment of fire on second floor, for the fire was only darkened in this area by Engine Company 1 in passing to the third floor.
   B. Engine Company 1 can not safely move to the third floor unless protected by another line. Since the fire was only darkened, it could again develop rapidly and cut off Engine Company 1. Therefore, this line is the backup or safety line.
   C. In case of a burst length of hose in the first line, the second line is in a position to protect men and complete the extinguishment of the fire.

4. Engine 3 assignment and reasons: Stretch a line up the aerial ladder to the top floor and move toward the rear.
   *Reasons:*
   A. The top floor fire will be more massive than on the lower floors, since it has been burning for a longer period of time without the quenching effects of water.
   B. The fire loading on the top floor is more severe, since the cockloft space contains great quantities of structural timbers and roofing boards.
   C. Life hazards are generally more severe on the top floor than on lower floors, because of higher temperatures and stratification of gases.
   D. These buildings generally do not collapse, but if the fire burns in the top floor area for an extended period, you can anticipate some roof failure.
   E. Unless the aerial is in use for lifesaving purposes, it is a means of providing quick access to the top floor for line advancement, and, with fire blowing out the rear windows, there will be an inflow of fresh air from the front, improving the chances of immediate line movement to the rear.
   F. Two lines are already in the interior stairway. This ordinarily should be the limit because stretching a third

line through this same artery could lead to confusion and a jamming of hose lines. It would retard the advancement of the first two lines. (Figure 3)

5. A. It takes too long to carry portable ladders to the rear of the building, since there is generally no direct access from the street to rear yards.
   B. The roof scuttles in the adjoining buildings are at times strongly nailed closed.
   C. It is the quickest and surest method.

6. The most effective battalion chiefs are those in the fire building. The action is on the fire floor and above. Coordinating engine and ladder companies in their fire duties is one of the principal duties of a battalion chief. He must not only coordinate line advancement with ventilation, but also make certain that engine company streams are supplementing each other and not working against each other. It is within the fire building that the battalion chief can best spark his men to maintain movement and advancement of lines. Under high heat conditions, it is extremely difficult to maintain movement of lines, but through encouragement and relief of personnel, the battalion chief can often be the difference between success and failure in fire operations.

The battalion chief must "get the feel of the fire" and its potentialities. He does this by checking the floor below the fire to determine floor layout, conditions in the rear, occupancies, shafts, and the exposure situation. He then checks the fire floor for size and intensity of fire, and generally follows this by going above the fire. In this manner, his reconnaissance will give him a rather complete picture of the problems that face him. Of course, his endeavors are not only to determine fire travel, but primarily to ascertain the life hazard in the building. The chief with the most facts will probably be the most effective in the command function.

The battalion chief generally responds with an aide. If not, an experienced fireman should be designated as his aide at the scene. The aide should have a walkie-talkie so that he can maintain communications with the battalion chief. It is the aide who should take the street position so that he can readily assign the incoming companies upon instructions from the battalion chief.

A deputy chief or higher officer should not ordinarily respond to first alarm operations. Of course, if the emergency has vast potentialities, the deputy chief or higher officer should respond as quickly as possible, to relieve the battalion chief of the overall command of the fire, thus enabling the battalion chief to concentrate on the operations inside the fire building.

In volunteer communities, command should be related to experience. In paid departments, it generally takes a man a minimum of 10 years to become a chief officer. The only way he is going to learn to use his experience is by commanding fire situations with a minimum of interference. His superiors should critique his fires and hold him responsible. This does not mean fault-finding, but rather the use of the coaching method of training to help him in his endeavors to become a more efficient commander.

Senior chief officers take on an aura of infallibility. If we could admit that our batting average at fire situations is not 1.000 but perhaps closer to .500, thus removing this imaginary cloak of infallibility, subordinates would have the opportunity to work in a reasonable climate, wherein they could be more concerned with progress than the possibility of making mistakes. If mistakes will not be tolerated, there will be no decisions and hence—no progress.

Subordinates should not be criticized for lack of decisiveness, failure of leadership, or stagnation if they are not given frequent opportunities to learn to lead, make decisions, develop their ideas and use initiative. If every mistake draws down the wrath of the superior, forget progress. However, the aspiring officers must be adequately supervised to prevent the reoccurrence of any mistake. Supervision is constructive and not demoralizing.

7. The strategic factor is the lack of exposure problems. Since no companies have to be committed to exposure protection, all companies are assigned to the fire building. This is exclusively an offensive strategy.

If the construction details included a light and air shaft between buildings, or an exposure to a rear building, then the strategy would be offensive-defensive, and a second alarm would have to be transmitted immediately.

This fire shows the advantages of knowing the structural details of common type buildings within a city or community, and how this knowledge assists the chief in quickly identifying strategic factors and formulating strategy.

# Chapter 5

# Conduction, Radiation and Convection

The objective of this chapter is to provide the student of fire strategy with a thorough understanding of heat transfer phenomena, since most fires spread by conduction, radiation or convection. There are many articles written on placement of lines and apparatus, but unless the author states the reasons for line positioning he is not providing the student with adequate knowledge. Since circumstances at fires are always somewhat different, line positioning will vary with these differences. Whether it is better to hit the fire building with a major stream or to develop a water curtain on the exposed building is related to the student's understanding of the transmission of heat. With a grasp of the subject of heat transfer not only will the fire strategist know *where* to position his units, but also *why*. And it is principally this *"why"* that constitutes the science of fire strategy. This chapter is highly technical and complex, and will require great diligence on the part of the student. To help the student master these principles, Chapter 6 will deal with fire situations in which the principles of conduction, radiation and convection will govern line positioning and use.

Heat may be transferred by one or more of these three methods:

1. Conduction, or the transfer of heat by contact of the molecules of a substance;
2. Convection, or the transfer of heat by circulation of a gas or liquid;
3. Radiation, or the transfer of heat by electromagnetic waves.

## CONDUCTION—DIRECT CONTACT

Heat is transferred by conduction from one body to another by contact between the two bodies. This is the simplest mode of heat transfer and is accomplished by the direct communication of molecular disturbance through a substance by means of the collisions of neighboring molecules. A steam pipe in contact with wood transfers its heat to the wood by actual touch. No movement of gases or radiant energy is needed. (Figure 1)

*GASES AND LIQUIDS*

There are large differences in the thermal conductivities of various materials. Gases have very low conductivity, hence they are very poor conductors of heat. In general, liquids also are quite poor conductors.

*SOLIDS*

The conductivity of solids varies over a wide range, from the very low values for asbestos fiber or brick to the relatively high values for most metals, notably silver or copper. (Figure 2)

*Thermal Conductivity of Common Substances*

| | |
|---|---|
| Silver | 2870 |
| Copper | 2660 |
| Aluminum | 1460 |

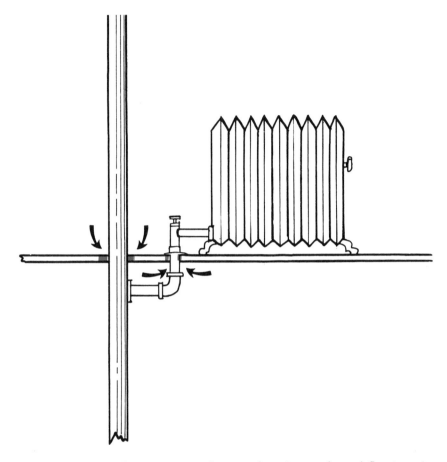

Figure 1.  *Red indicates contacts between hot pipes and wood flooring where ignition can occur.*

| | |
|---|---|
| Steel | 320 |
| Oak | 140 |
| Concrete | 12 |
| Glass | 7 |
| Brick | 5 |
| Water | 4.1 |
| Hydrogen | 1.1 |
| Cork board | 0.3 |
| Glass wool | .27 |
| Air | .15 |

Figure 2.   *Contrast is shown between wood and metal cabinets as conductors.*

Transmission of heat cannot be completely stopped by any insulating material. The flow of water can be stopped by closing a valve; but, regardless of its thickness or type, heat-insulating material can only slow the rate of heat transmission, not stop it. For this reason there should always be an air space or some way of carrying the heat away rather than reliance solely on heat-insulating material. The chart shows which materials are the best insulators.

### CONDUCTION FACTORS

The amount of heat transferred is dependent upon the thickness of the material, the temperature differential between the point of contact and departure, the thermal conductivity of the material and the total amount of time exposed. If the rate of heat conducted exceeds the rate of heat dissipated, there will be temperature buildup. Continued over a sufficient period of time, the ignition temperature of the material can be reached.

### STEAM PIPES AND WOOD

Tests made by the National Bureau of Standards on thin shavings of wood indicated an ignition temperature range of about 440° to 550° F. For larger pieces of wood, the ignition temperature is probably closer to 750° F. Yet, there are records of a considerable number of fires that have been caused by low-pressure steam pipes in contact with wood. This provides fairly conclusive evidence that long continued heating at temperatures as low as 212° F can cause the ignition of wood under favorable conditions.

### GENERAL MOTORS FIRE—LAVONIA, MICHIGAN

The historical General Motors, Livonia, Michigan fire presents an outstanding example of heat conduction as the principal cause of fire spread.

### FIRE BUILDING

The exterior walls were steel frame with brick and glass. A steel deck roof was supported by unprotected steel girders, trusses, and columns. The steel deck was covered with asphalt felt and roofing paper, all mopped with 2000 tons of asphalt, tar and pitch.

The building was 870 feet wide, one story high, and had an undivided floor area of approximately 1,500,000 sq. ft. The contents for the most part were noncombustible, since the plant manufactured car transmissions.

Twenty percent of the building area was protected with automatic sprinklers. Hydrants were well dispersed throughout the grounds and were fed from a 200,000-gallon gravity tank.

*ORIGIN AND SPREAD OF FIRE (Figure 3)*

A welder's spark ignited contents of a drip pan high above the floor. The oil had a flash point of 97.7° F. The portable extinguishing equipment could not be used effectively because of the height of the drip pan and the fire spread to other drip pans near the ceiling. In the meantime, the heat was being conducted through the steel deck, melting the asphalt, tar and pitch. Within 10 minutes, the molten tar began to seep through the joints of the metal roof deck to spread fire below. The molten tar dropped from the roof deck 100 feet or more in advance of the actual fire. At the beginning, the fire was not continuous, but spot fires soon joined and a major fire was in progress.

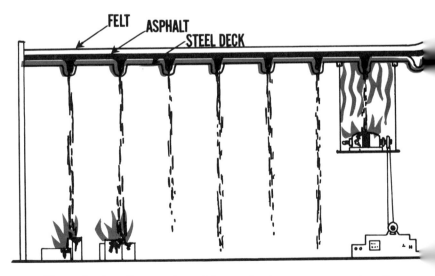

Figure 3.   *Roofing tar, heated by conduction, starts secondary fires.*

The fire companies stretched to the interior of the building. However, there were no roof vents, and therefore the heavy black smoke and the highly heated products of combustion mushroomed to the floor level. The companies had no alternative but to withdraw from the building. Under the described conditions, fire personnel only have a few minutes in which to darken the fire, for under severe heat conditions the unprotected metal members will expand, buckle and collapse.

You can imagine the ineffectiveness of an exterior attack. Streams were projected through windows and doors, but the maximum reach was approximately 50–60 feet, and the width of the building was 870 feet.

The building was completely lost. General Motors' major transmission plant was out of operation. It was estimated, when all of the losses were considered, that this was a $500 million casualty.

There were many factors that contributed to the spread of this fire, but the principal contributing factor was the heat conducted through the steel deck that melted the tar, which in turn dripped through the steel joints, spreading the fire 100 feet and more away from the original fire. This all happened so quickly that when the fire companies arrived, the fire area was too extensive for an effective interior attack. The structural deficiencies were so great that roof collapse was imminent.

## RADIATION

Radiation is the emission of heat energy in the form of electromagnetic waves from the surface of a heated body. These waves travel at the speed of light and pass through air without being significantly impaired. These heat radiations are invisible and may pre-heat an exposed building to the point of ignition before the danger is recognized. Radiated heat travels in straight lines.

### HEAT-REFLECTION, TRANSMISSION, ABSORPTION

Heat is radiated as electromagnetic waves and as these waves travel outward from the source, one of three things will happen:

1. A portion of the radiation may be reflected.
2. A portion of the radiation may be transmitted or passed through the material.
3. A portion of the radiation may be absorbed.

These portions that are reflected or transmitted continue on and do not heat the materials through which they pass. However, the portion that is absorbed is converted to heat, increasing the temperature of the material and thereby introducing the hazard of ignition.

Radiated heat will readily pass through gaseous substances and to some extent certain liquids and solids which are transparent to heat radiation. On the other hand, opaque solid substances, even in thin sheets, will absorb or reflect radiated heat.

Rough surfaces absorb better than smoothly polished surfaces. Therefore, wood with a dark rough surface will ignite much more readily than wood with a light-colored smooth surface.

Ordinary window glass will transmit radiant energy. However, experiences have shown that a thin film of water over window glass stops some of the radiant energy and is more effective than a curtain of water in the air in preventing the transmission of heat through exposed windows.

For exposed buildings with brick masonry or other incombustible exterior walls, the exposure hazard depends in large part upon the size and area of the windows.

### TEMPERATURE

The quantity of energy radiated increases rapidly with the temperature. The quantity of radiation emitted from a source is proportional to the fourth power of the absolute temperature of the source.

A high rate of radiant heat transferred in a short time is more dangerous than the same amount radiated over a longer period of time. A dangerous temperature will be reached more quickly at the higher absorption rate. In this brief interval, little of the heat can be conducted away from the surface or removed by convection currents. For this reason, thick materials are more difficult to ignite than thin materials. For a similar reason, poor heat conductors, such as wood or paper, ignite more readily than good heat conductors. The danger to an exposed building will be greatly increased when there is a large number of thin, easily ignited points of ignition.

### DISTANCE (Figure 4)

Distance is probably the most important factor in exposure protection since the amount of radiated heat reaching a surface will vary considerably with the distance between the exposed surface and the source of the radiated heat.

A fire of small dimensions, even if intense, is called a point source. The intensity of heat radiation from a point source varies inversely with the square of the distance. For example, the amount or intensity of radiated heat reaching an exposed surface 40 feet away will be only one-fourth of that reaching a surface 20 feet away.

The intensity of heat radiation diminishes with distance. If the flame front is in the form of a long line with little height, it is considered a line source. The intensity or amount of radiant heat reaching an exposed surface will vary inversely as the distance from a line source. For example, at 40 feet, the intensity reaching an exposed surface will be only one-half of that at 20 feet.

If the flame front has considerable height and width, such as in a conflagration, it can be considered an area source. Radiant heat intensity from an area source diminishes with distance but it diminishes very little because distances are small compared to flame height and width.

The transmission of radiated heat can take place over long distances. Buildings have been ignited at distances of 1000 feet from large fires. Nuclear explosions will ignite buildings more than 10 miles from the explosion and skin burns will be sustained more than 12 miles from the explosion. In dealing with radiant heat energy, the fire fighter must contend with a potent force.

As a matter of fact, the elementary features of distance have long been recognized as necessary to the prevention of exposure fires. Following the conflagration, which destroyed Rome in 64 A.D., Nero's construction code contained the following passage:

"After marking out his own domain, the ground which Nero left to the public was not laid out for a new city in a hurry and without judgment. A regular plan was formed. The streets were made wide and long. The height of houses was so fixed with an open area before the doors and porticos to secure and adorn the front. The houses were built on a new principle, raised to a certain height without beams or woodwork on arches of stone from the quarries of Alba. Those materials would be impervious

Figure 4. *The truck fire represents a point source, the brush fire, a line source and the conflagration, an area source.*

and of a nature as to resist the forces of fire. The springs of water which before that time had been intercepted by individuals for their separate use were no longer suffered to be diverted from their channels, though were left to the care of commissioners so that the public might be properly supplied, and in the case of fire for reservoirs at hand to stop the progress of the mischief. It was also decreed that houses should no longer be contiguous with slight party walls to divide them, but that every house was to stand detached, surrounded and insulated by its own enclosure. These several regulations were perhaps the best that human wisdom could suggest.''

This passage sounds familiar since it includes some of the ideas which are now incorporated in modern building codes. For example, included are: a clear space between buildings, fire-resistant construction, adequate water supplies, authority to control the water supply, detached buildings, dividing walls between buildings and other methods to control the spread of fire.

### ATMOSPHERIC CONDITIONS

Other important factors in exposure protection are atmospheric conditions, particularly the amount of smoke and water vapor in the air. Particles of dust, smoke or water droplets in the atmosphere absorb radiation to some degree but their main impact is to scatter radiation. Radiated heat is emitted from the source regardless of the direction of the wind. However, on the leeward side of conflagrations, heat radiated downward from the sloping column of hot convection gases may ignite the roofs of buildings, the upper portions of stores or the tar surfaces of streets.

### MOISTURE CONTENT

Moisture content is another factor in delaying ignition of an exposed substance. The higher the moisture content, the more difficult it is for a substance to be ignited. Wood and similar materials are not easily ignited when their moisture content is greater than 15 percent. However, once a fire is well under way, the significance of the moisture factor reduces, since the heat radiation and, therefore, the rate of pyrolysis, increases. Under such conditions, wood will burn with a moisture content of 50 percent or more.

*SUMMARY*

To summarize, the ease of ignition of exposed material by radiated heat is dependent upon: (1) the distance between the ignition source and the exposure, (2) the absolute temperature of the ignition source, (3) the thickness of the exposed material, (4) the surface (rough or smooth) of the exposed material, (5) the color of the exposed material, (6) the moisture content of the exposed material. A study of some notable fires that have spread beyond the building of origin will show the effects of radiated heat.

*CHARLES RIVER FIRE—OCT. 3, 1946 (Figure 5)*

At a point where the Charles River is about 80 feet wide as it flows between Wellesley and Newton, Mass., there were two old wooden mills that made textile products from wool shoddy. One plant was on the Wellesley bank of the river and the other was on the Newton bank.

The Wellesley plant was two stories high and had a 300-foot frontage on the river. The Newton plant varied in height from two to three stories and had a 400-foot frontage on the river. Neither plant had exposure protection and both were built so close to the water that fire fighters were unable to operate from the river side.

Fire started at the Wellesley plant, quickly flashed over the lint-covered ceiling and soon overtaxed an ancient and inadequate sprinkler system. Fire fighting had to be conducted from the land side only, as fire fighters were unable to gain positions on the river side. Therefore, the rear of the structure burned almost unchecked. There was no attempt to control fire in the rear of the building.

The exposed wooden buildings across the river became ignited and one of them was totally destroyed. A second building was saved by an interior automatic sprinkler system and in the third building, the operation of automatic closing shutters in a brick wall prevented fire from extending into that building. In this case the cause of fire extension to the Newton plant was probably radiated heat. Radiant heat energy emitted by the unchecked fire in the rear of the plant crossed the 80-foot-wide river and ignited the wooden building opposite. The vertical exposing wall surfaces, two stories high and 400 feet long, offered an ideal target for this uncontrolled radiant heat energy. (Figure 5).

Figure 5. *Fire started in mill on left bank of the Charles River. Convection heat for the most part spiralled skyward, so it was the radiant heat which ignited buildings on the opposite bank.*

### *MEMPHIS BALL PARK FIRE (Figure 6)*

The Russwood Ball Park grandstand in Memphis, Tenn., was wood construction with a wood-on-steel frame roof. The roof decking was covered by 14 layers of asphalt-impregnated roofing material applied during the 39 years it existed.

The fire began in an accumulation of trash below the grandstand and quickly spread. Fanned by a brisk 23-mph wind, the fire soon involved the entire structure as well as seven retail stores on the fringes of the ball park.

Radiant heat, hot gases, and burning embers carried across a 100-foot thoroughfare to expose a 13-story, fire-resistant hospital. The hospital sustained severe heat exposure and some structural damage. Radiant heat alone ignited the window frames of a maternity wing across a 45-foot alley from the grandstand. This maternity wing was of fire-resistant construction and fires in the window frames were contained by interior hand lines operated from the standpipe system. The ignition by radiant heat

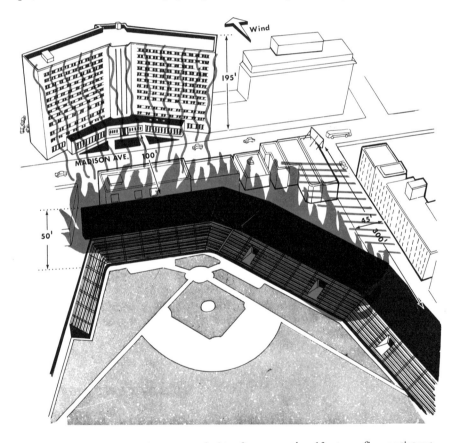

Figure 6. *The principal target of this fire was the 13-story fire resistant hospital. Prevention of a major disaster can be attributed to superior building construction, especially the thermal pane window glass in aluminum sash.*

at a distance of 45 feet required the average temperature of the burning grandstand to be about 1700° F. Fortunately, there was little or no fire spread within the wing even though windows were broken out. Total evacuation of the building was not necessary.

The main hospital was over twice as far from the fire as the maternity wing, but the main hospital sustained greater structural damage. Although the radiant heat per square foot was one-fourth of that at the maternity building, the convected heat was many times greater. The wind gusts made the difference. The wind increased from 23 mph to even higher velocities to carry the superheated gases from the grandstand to the exposed hospital.

This wind-driven heat broke out ordinary plate glass windows on the first floor and allowed fire to extend to furnishings and draperies in the lobby, public restaurant and administrative offices. Fire fighters were able to control and extinguish these fires quickly with hand lines operated from the standpipe system.

Fortunately, the windows on other floors were of the thermal pane type, which consists of two panes of glass with an insulating airspace between them. All these windows were in aluminum sash. Although the thermal pane windows are not designed to resist fire, they kept the fire out of the building. Many cracked but none completely broke out. The aluminum sash on upper floors warped, which indicated a temperature in excess of 1000° F there.

The fire attack concentrated on the use of heavy streams to contain the fire to the ball park and adjacent retail stores. Positions were maintained on the windward side because the leeward side of the fire was untenable. If the hospital buildings had been of wooden construction, it is highly unlikely that they could have been saved.


## CONVECTION

Convection is the transfer of heat by the circulation of heated matter. There must be a circulating medium involved; usually this will be either a gas or a liquid. In the case of a liquid, it can be the heated water rising in a household heating system. In the case of a gas, it can be the heated air expanding and rising from a fire.

### SPREAD OF FIRE

Fire fighters confront convection currents in their commonest form as the heated smoke and gases rising from a fire. The smoke produced at a fire behaves in much the same way as heated air or any heated gas. The hotter the smoke becomes, the faster it will expand and rise. Smoke at fires can be raised to temperatures in excess of 1000° F. As it rises through a building, smoke gives up its heat to surfaces it contacts. This in turn can cause the ignition of combustible material. In this instance, the heated smoke and gases act as the circulating medium for the transfer of heat by convection, which is a common cause for the extension of fires in a building.

At large fires, these heated gases are released in great volume and can contain millions of British thermal units. These super-heated gases will extend fire to exposed combustible materials. They are capable of igniting fires in exposed buildings as they sweep along their sides and windows. The intense heat causes windows to break out and the heated gases soon ignite exposed combustibles.

### ROOF VENTILATION

The techniques of ventilation at fires depend to a great extent upon the transfer of heat by convection. Since it is natural for heated smoke and gases released by fire to expand and rise in a vertical direction, a high priority must be given to roof ventilation.

### CELLAR FIRES

When the smoke is dense and the heat within reasonable limits, fire fighters with self-contained breathing apparatus and fog streams can successfully cope with convection currents. But fires can burn with intensity in cellar and sub-cellar levels and these areas become furnace-like in their temperatures. Convection prevents progress of fire fighters. Under these circumstances, vertical channels must be used to move the flow of convection currents from the cellar levels so that firemen can move into the fire area with their hose streams. At times, cellar pipes or distributors can be used from the floor above to cool a cellar fire. At other times, the floor above is not tenable. Some fire departments are becoming proficient in the use of mechanical equipment to eject convected heat.

### BACK DRAFTS

A back draft is a devastating phenomenon which is sometimes called a smoke explosion or a hot-air explosion. It is the ignition and rapid combustion of flammable gases produced by a fire. Conditions building up to a back draft take time and depend on the behavior of heat as it is transmitted by convection currents.

Layers of combustible gases generated by a fire build up or mushroom in an enclosure or building. These gases are heated and continue to be heated by further gases released by the fire. If left unvented, they are soon heated to their ignition temperature and need only the right mixture of air to burn. This heating is continued by the convected heat emanating from the fire and is a major cause of fire spread in buildings. Sometimes there is insufficient air or oxygen to support combustion. Then convected heat continues to keep these gases heated above their ignition temperature. Later, a window may break or a door is opened, and there is a rush of air to these gases. If the mix is proper, a devastating explosion follows.

### FIREPROOF CONSTRUCTION

In fireproof construction, the convected heat is frequently confined to the fire floor. In these cases, the heat is absorbed by the partitions leading to the stairwells. If the fire is intense, the heat may prevent fire fighters from advancing to the seat of the fire. In smaller fires, cross-ventilation on the fire floor will release convected heat.

In the Hotel La Salle fire of June 5, 1946, in Chicago, convected heat from a fire that started in the lobby swept to the upper floors by means of the powerful, flue-like actions of the 22-story open stairways.

All of the 61 victims died as a result of anoxia and carbon monoxide poisoning. The smoke and gases not only filled the corridors, but were drawn into the guest rooms where transoms

Figure 7. *The deadly gases rise in a 22-story open stairway to claim 61 victims.*

or doors were open. Most of the deaths occurred below the seventh floor, indicating that the smoke and heat lost their buoyancy and started to stratify at this level.

### TIMES TOWER FIRE—NEW YORK CITY *(Figure 8)*

However, in the Times Tower fire in New York City in 1961, convection gases traveled from a subcellar to the 22nd floor. The fire originated at the third level of the subcellar in some very combustible stock in a 50 x 110-foot area. Because of its inaccessibility, the fire burned for hours without the quenching

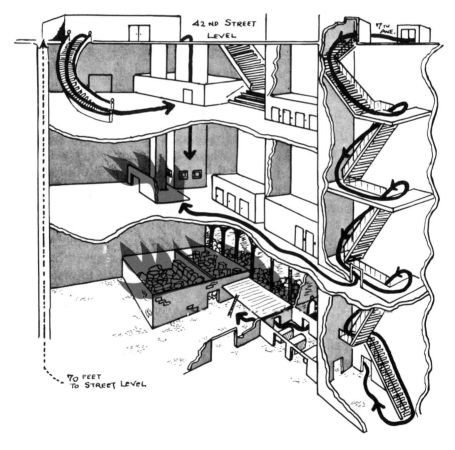

Figure 8. *Fire was confined to cellar areas but the toxic gases killed two firemen on the 22nd floor.*

effects of water. Toxic gases permeated the upper floors of the building and the elevator shaft.

Two firemen on their search and ventilation mission were overcome by these toxic gases on the 22nd floor, and resuscitation failed to revive them. A maintenance man trapped in an elevator car became a victim of these same gases. This fire never extended out of the subcellar level.

### HOTEL ROOSEVELT FIRE—JACKSONVILLE, FLORIDA (Figure 9)

In Hotel Roosevelt in Jacksonville, Fla., on Dec. 29, 1963, fire originated in the first floor ballroom but convection currents carried deadly gases from the concealed space above the lobby ceiling to the attic. Of the 20 persons who died of asphyxiation, eight were on the 13th floor.

### VERTICAL RISE OF CONVECTION GASES

To what height will convection gases rise in tall structures? The building has not yet been constructed that will confine fire and convection gases to the floor of origin. Utility shafts run the height of a building. Since repairs are a constant feature of maintenance, defects in shaft enclosures will often develop, and access doors or panels to these shafts are, at times, substandard in their safety features. There is no fire-stopping at floor levels in the shafts, so that convected heat and gases have a vertical artery built right into the structure in which to disperse death to upper floors.

In recent fires in new high-rise structures, smoke has permeated upward throughout the entire height of the structure, principally through the stair and elevator shafts and the central air-conditioning system.

### FIRE FATALITIES

Actual statistics on the causes of fire deaths are not always available, but it is recognized that fire fatalities from the inhalation of hot fire gases and hot air are far more common causes of fire deaths than all other causes combined. In practically all instances of fires with large loss of life, the primary cause of the life loss was the inhalation of heated and

Figure 9. *People shown in the windows were not directly endangered by flame, but the toxic gases claimed many victims.*

toxic fire gases. The next fire will show how rapidly convection currents can victimize occupants in a fire building.

*NURSING HOME FIRE*

A three-story and basement wooden dwelling with open stairways was used for a nursing home in Hudson, Mass. Fire broke out in a closet in the rear of the second-floor hall on Dec. 20, 1962. The fire was detected by an automatic fire detection system connected through an auxiliary fire alarm box to fire department headquarters. Three on-duty men started their three-minute run to the fire with two pumpers and a ladder truck. The chief ordered a 1½-inch pre-connected line up the rear stairway. The fire was knocked down quickly—less than 15 minutes after the operation of the automatic alarm system. Nurses, police and firemen were able to remove about 33 patients or employees from the various floors. Although fire operations were efficient and evacuation procedures started as soon as a loud gong sounded throughout the building, nine elderly patients lost their lives. Some were burned, but most died of asphyxiation.

*LOS ANGELES SCHOOL TESTS*

From April 16 to June 30, 1959, the Los Angeles City Fire Department conducted a series of school fire tests. The findings were published in a book, "Operation School Building," published by the National Fire Protection Association. The tests showed that untenable smoke conditions were reached in two to seven minutes on at least one entire floor above the fire. Automatic heat devices detected the presence of fire at about the same time that untenable smoke conditions were reached within the building. Under the test conditions, this would not allow sufficient time for safe evacuation of a three-story school building.

In nursing homes and hospitals, evacuation would be much slower than in school buildings because of the age and infirmity of the patients.

Another conclusion reached in these school tests is that where the stairways are open, only a complete system of automatic sprinklers will maintain low temperatures throughout the building and reduce the buildup of smoke and irritating gases. This was the only form of fire protection found to be satisfactory. All other forms of fire protection were found to be inadequate to cope with convection currents.

It has been established that from the time of the inception of fire to the arrival of fire department units takes a minimum of 10 minutes. Fatalities from convection will continue to plague the fire fighting force unless a fully automatic sprinkler system is provided for all buildings where vertical channels permit the flow of toxic heated gases to upper floors. In nonfireproof nursing homes and hospitals, since the problems of evacuation are multiplied, a fully automatic sprinkler system is essential for life protection.

### *CONVECTION IN RESPECT TO EXPOSURES*

We have largely considered convection from the viewpoint of the dangers of the gases inside buildings. It is the principal medium by which fires spread on the fire floor and to upper floors, and it causes the greatest number of fire fatalities.

Its awesome energy contributes greatly to exposure problems. This will be emplified by describing the key features of the Burlington fire.

### *BURLINGTON FIRE (Figure 10)*

This fire occurred in Chicago in 1922 and is significant since it clearly shows the distances through which the elements of fire will travel and jeopardize even fireproof buildings.

### *EXPOSING BUILDINGS*

One building that burned was seven stories high with a 28-foot frontage and the other was two stories high with a 50-foot frontage. Their construction was combustible.

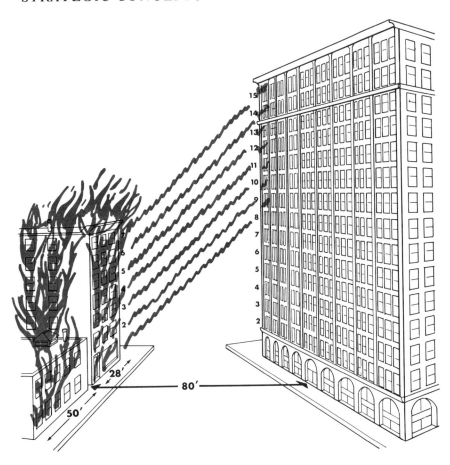

Figure 10.   *Convected heat can cause unexpected problems at the upper floors of exposed buildings, even in structures 80 or more feet away.*

### EXPOSURE—BURLINGTON BUILDING

A fire-resistant office building, the Burlington Building was 15 stories, or 195 feet, high. There were large windows of plain glass, except along fire excapes, where there was wire glass.

### START OF FIRE

At 12:50 p.m., the Chicago Fire Department responded and found that fire had been in progress for some time in the exposing buildings. A defensive attack was necessary. At 1:30 a.m., the walls of the seven-story building completely collapsed.

### HEAT UNITS

It was computed that the exposing buildings were emitting heat at about 4 million Btu per second rate, of which about seven-eighths was hot air and products of combustion. Radiant heat which impinged on the Burlington Building was too little to set combustibles afire, through the plain glass windows.

### WIND

A 12–14 mph wind was blowing toward the exposed building. The hot gases rising vertically and the horizontal wind then combined to form an air current at about a 35 to 40-degree angle from the ground.

*Width of Street*—80 feet.

*Results*

1. The lower seven floors of the Burlington Building remained undamaged except for broken plain glass windows. The wire glass windows at the fire escape remained intact below the 9th floor.
2. The upper eight floors were fully involved in separate and distinct fires. Some of the wire glass windows actually melted and the glass ran out of frames onto sills and adjacent radiators.

### FIRE EXTINGUISHMENT

The fire was fought with hose lines off inside standpipes or brought up the two stairs. The structural damage was not too extensive.

It was assumed that the average temperature of the convection heat from the burning buildings was 1500° above the ambient temperature. The fire temperature most likely was higher, but when the gases mixed with air, they cooled somewhat. When the fire buildings collapsed, the amount of heat transmitted was at its height, for now there were no enclosing walls to contain the heat.

The fact that the wire glass windows melted and flowed gives good indication of the temperature of the convection currents as they were sweeping along walls and windows of the exposed building 80 feet from the fire.

It is worthy of note that convection heat, unlike radiant heat, does not travel in straight lines. The gases rise because of their buoyancy and the angle at which they rise is related to the velocity of the wind. It can be deduced that the convection heat emitted from the first floor of the fire buildings transmitted its devastating effects to the eighth floor of the exposed building.

The following concepts were learned, or their ideas were reinforced, from a study of this historic fire:

1. Even though the exposed building is fireproof and is separated by a clear space of 80 feet, this in itself is not adequate protection for the exposure.
2. Since convection heat rises as it traverses clear spaces, the upper floors of exposed buildings are in greater danger than the lower floors. The greater the wind velocity, the greater the angle at which convection currents will flow. This poses a serious problem on fire department operations since we are better equipped to cope with fire on the lower than the upper levels of tall structures.

### UNCONTROLLED CONVECTION CURRENTS

In fires that were previously discussed, the loss of life, and the complicated fire problems can be principally attributed to the uncontrolled flow of convection currents. This gives rise to this thought: control convection currents and the problems of fire fatalities and fire extension will miraculously diminish. And this is exactly what did occur in one of the most potentially dangerous fires ever fought.

### HOLLAND TUNNEL FIRE—NEW YORK CITY (Figure 11)

This fire occurred at 8:45 a.m., May 13, 1949, in one of the tubes of the Holland Tunnel under the Hudson River between

New York and Jersey City. It originated in a stalled truck loaded with about 50,000 pounds of carbon disulfide. The fire soon spread to nine other trucks, which contained, among other items, turpentine, alcohol, household bleach, wax, paper rolls, and of course, the gasoline in vehicle fuel tanks.

There were more than 100 vehicles behind the trucks on fire and an unknown number of persons were trapped in the tube. The carbon disulphide drums were exploding, the tunnel's lights went out, and almost total darkness prevailed. The devastation was such that the inner walls and ceiling were destroyed for a

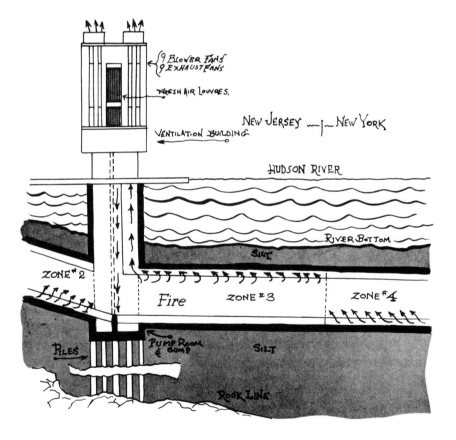

Figure 11. *Holland Tunnel fire. The controlled ventilation system made it possible to extinguish this very hot fire. The fire service should expore the technologies that will develop systems for regulating the environment at fires.*

distance of 600 feet. The chief in charge was appalled at the possibilities—and especially the fear that the Hudson River might pour its unlimited water into the tube.

The two separate tubes of the Holland Tunnel are interconnected at three locations. The two traffic lanes of each tube are approximately 9,200 feet long, with a headroom of $13^1/_2$ feet and ceilings of five inches of reinforced concrete. The tunnel is protected by a standpipe system.

Four ventilation buildings supply 84 five-speed fans, 42 exhaust and 42 intake, which are capable of changing air within the tunnel every $1^1/_2$ minutes. The system is divided into seven independent sections in each tube, with three intake and three exhaust fans for each section. The fresh air duct is below the tunnel roadway and the exhaust duct is in the ceiling.

A powerful poison, carbon disulfide is used very cautiously as a fumigant in grain elevators, warehouses and museums. Because of its rapid rate of volatility, low flash point ($-22°$ F) and wide flammable range (1 to 50 percent) carbon disulfide is one of the most dangerous of common chemicals. The Underwriters' Laboratories in its numerical classification of flammable liquids gives carbon disulfide a rating of 110+, while gasoline and ether are 95–100, and kerosine is 40. It boils at 114° F and evolves vapors that are about 2.6 times heavier than air.

The fire was approximately 2900 feet from the New Jersey entrance. The New Jersey fire fighters entered the tube, but their operations were seriously impeded by the 100 automobiles, buses and trucks behind the burning vehicles. They found it necessary to carry 2¹/₂-inch hose lines into the tunnel and to connect to standpipe facilities. Tunnel emergency crews were removing the vehicles while the fire was being attacked.

The New York City companies were able to drive their pumping equipment to within 300 feet of the fire. Lines were connected to the standpipe system. It is estimated that over 100 units of self-contained breathing apparatus were used at this fire. Although the liquid carbon disulfide continued to explode and chlorine fumes were being released by the bleach solution, fire fighters were able to remove their breathing equipment within one-half hour. The main body of fire was under control in a relatively short period of time once lines were operational. The main structure of the tunnel was not damaged. There were many smoke inhalation cases, but there were no fatalities. The firemen suffered more from the heat and their laborious efforts than from the fumes.

### SUCCESSFUL SOLUTION

As stated previously, the tube was divided into seven distinct sections for ventilation and each section had its own exhaust and blower fans. Upon notification of fire, the blower fans in the fire area were shut down and the speed of the exhaust fans were accelerated. In the adjacent sections, the exhaust fans were shut down, and the speed of the blower fans was accelerated. This created a longitudinal flow of air toward the fire area from each end of the tube, thus minimizing the spread of convection currents to other sections.

### CONCLUSION

*With this type of ventilating system the fire chief can control the flow of convection currents and thereby control his fire. This technique is adaptable not only to tunnels, but also to buildings and especially to windowless and high-rise structures.*

*All concerned with improvement of fire control and life safety should concentrate their efforts on the development of feasible fire ventilating systems for such structures.*

# Chapter 6

# Fire Susceptibility of Different Types of Construction

In this chapter three fire situations are presented. In the Ace Waste Paper fire, the objectives are principally concerned with heat conduction and collapse of brick-joist structures. In the Tire Company fire, the objectives are principally concerned with radiation and collapse of fire-proof structures, while the Paragon Paint fire has as its principal objectives a discussion of water curtains at large fires and their use in protecting against radiant and convection heat.

## ACE WASTE PAPER COMPANY FIRE

*CONSTRUCTION (Figure 1)*

The building is of brick-joist construction 25 X 100 feet and five stories high with bearing walls of 8-inch unpierced masonry. The stairway is unenclosed and its structural members are principally of wood. Although the front and rear windows are protected by metal shutters, many shutters are open.

*OCCUPANCY*

The building is occupied by a single tenant and used exclusively for the storage and baling of waste paper.

*EXPOSED BUILDING*

The 40 X 100-foot exposed building is six stories high and of fireproof construction. The Bernet Art Gallery uses the building for storing oil paintings and antiques. The walls facing the fire building are 8-inch unpierced brick except for the top floor, which has three shuttered windows overlooking the roof of the fire building.

An automatic sprinkler system fully protects this exposure. However, the only water supply is a 5000-gallon gravity tank 20 feet above the roof and supported by unprotected metal members.

There are no other exposures.

*FIRE SITUATION*

The time of the fire is 2 a.m. There is no life hazard. There is a 12-mph wind blowing in the direction of the exposed building. Fire originated on the first floor of the paper warehouse and has extended to all the upper floors via the unenclosed stairs. The heat cracked the skylight glass and the flames surge through impinging on the shutters of the exposed building. (Figure 1).

*RESPONSE*

Two 1000-gpm engine companies and an aerial platform company. Each company has five firefighters.

Figure 1. *The master stream of the aerial platform is alternated to especially protect the gravity tank of the exposed building and the top floor shutters.*

## QUESTIONS

1. What is the structural stability of brick-joist construction in a fire of this intensity?

*2. What are the contributing factors to the collapse of these walls?*

*3. In respect to heat conduction, where in the exposed building is the hazard greatest and why?*

*4. Assign Engine Company 1 and state your justifications.*

5. *Where would you position the aerial platform and what is the intended purposes of its master stream?*

6. *The remaining ladder personnel are assigned to the exposed building. What are their duties?*

7. *Engine 2 has already fed the aerial platform unit. Now, how would you use the available personnel of Engines 1 and 2?*

*8. What are the strategic factors in this fire?*

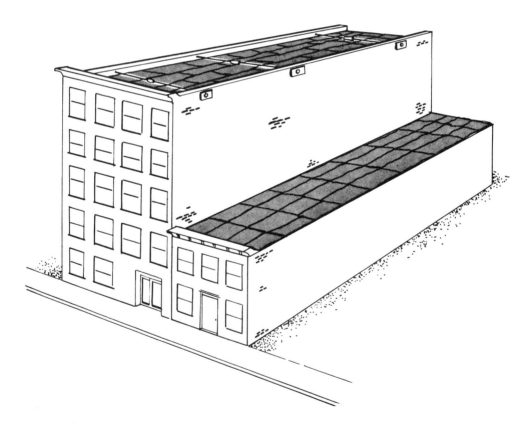

Figure 2.  *National Bureau of Standards test buildings. Note how tie-rods were installed to delay collapse of the walls. The sheet metal roofs were used to minimize the danger of flying brands.*

1. This construction is frequently termed quick-burning. Floors of two-ply one-inch matched sheathing boards will withstand a major fire for about 15 minutes. The fire, therefore, will not only extend to the upper floors by means of the unenclosed stairs, but will burn through the floor boards and extend in a mass to each of the upper floors. In this type of construction and occupancy, when one floor is fully involved and the fire has been burning for about 15 to 20 minutes, collapse of the structure can be anticipated.

Figure 3. *A section of the front wall of the National Bureau of Standards test building collapsed 28 minutes after start of fire. 11 minutes later the major portion of all walls had collapsed, and debris buried the 2-story adjoining building.*

In 1928, at Washington, D.C., the National Bureau of Standards conducted the following test:

A five-story brick-joist building, 30 X 75 feet, and a two-story brickjoist building, 20 X 75 feet, were used for the test. Each building had an open stairway and an open elevator shaft. There was no basement in either building. The floors in each building had ordinary wooden joists supporting one-inch flooring. The exterior walls of the buildings were well-laid brick of a thickness greater than required by the standard regulations. The buildings were stocked with waste lumber to represent a combustible occupancy. Several safes were distributed throughout the structures to create a condition similar to that encountered in an actual fire. (Figure 2)

Both buildings were provided with sheetmetal roofs and no lumber smaller than one-inch boards was used in the buildings to minimize the danger from flying sparks and firebrands.

The exterior walls of the five-story building were held together with $1^1/_2$-inch steel tie-rods, installed above the roof, to delay the collapse of the walls, which were expected to fall outward as a result of the expansion of the interior surface when subjected to the heat.

At 5:30 A.M., several fires were started simultaneously on the ground floors of both buildings. A few gallons of kerosene were used.

At about 5:35 a.m., the fire extended to the top floor of the five-story building and shortly after this, both buildings were fully involved.

At about 5:48 a.m., the wooden floor joists began to burn through and safes began to drop.

At 5:58 a.m., a section of the front wall of the five-story building fell outward. (Figure 3)

At 6:15 a.m., the major portions of all walls had collapsed, the side wall of the five-story building buried the two-story building and created a very hot, smoldering ruin.

A large force of the Washington Fire Department surrounded these buildings to protect neighboring structures. Thermometers recorded temperatures as high as 2400°F.

2. A. Brick is a good insulator, and since its thermal conductivity is low, the temperature on the inside of the wall will be extremely high. Since heat conductivity through the wall is low, the difference in the temperature between the inside and outside is great. Therefore, the inside of the wall will expand. This will cause the wall to curve

outward and fall away from the building. If exterior streams are played against the exterior wall, this cooling action will accelerate the collapse.

B. In baled paper occupancies, the floor loads of the machinery used for baling and the baled paper are of such magnitude that the floor beams will fail under these fire conditions. If the floor beams are not selfreleasing, the levering action will cause wall failure. (Figure 4)

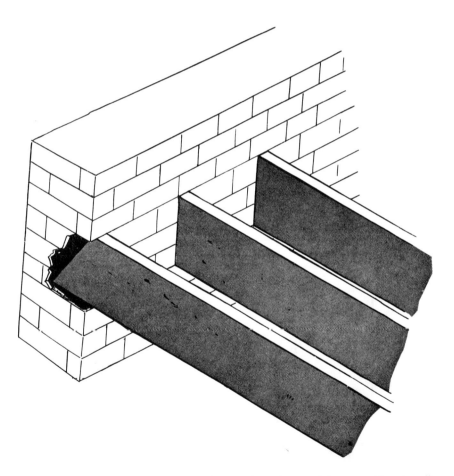

Figure 4. *Angular cut of beam ends permits release of beams without wall failure.*

Figure 5. *This cartoon represents the artist's conception of wall expansion due to water absorption of waste paper stock.*

C. The burning away of the floors, and the failure of the floor beams will considerably weaken the exterior walls, which thereby lose their side supports.

D. In older brick buildings, the lime and cement binding the brick disintegrate with time and further weaken under such fire conditions. The hazard is accentuated by hose streams, which wash loose mortar out of the joints and further destroy stability.

E. Once floor beams start to fail, the action becomes progressive, since the heavy bales and machnery will crash to the floor below, imposing a tremendous successive impact load on each lower floor level.

F. Baled paper and vegetable fibers asborb water rapidly. This has two distinct hazards in terms of structural stability. First, the bulk of the material will expand when soaked by fire streams and, in situations where the storage does not provide for adequate clearance, this expansion has been known to push out exterior walls. Furthermore, water absorption will considerably increase floor loading and threaten beam failure. (Figure 5)

3. From the first to fifth floors, there are 16 inches of brick separating the fire building from the exposed building. Heat of long duration and of this intensity will penetrate any solid mass. The rate at which it penetrates depends on the thermal conductivity of the solid material and the duration, area and intensity of the fire. The collapse of the fire building will diminish the heat conduction hazard, since it decreases the duration of heat exposure.

With the flame inpinging on the shutters, the rate of heat conduction through the shutters will be astronomical since metal has a much greater heat conductivity than brick and is much thinner as well. The inner facing of the shutter will radiate heat which will quickly penetrate the glass windows.

Further, with flame impinging upon a shutter under such grave conditions, the shutter itself may warp and fail.

4. Feed sprinkler siamese with two large-diameter hose lines. Justification:

    A. Gravity tank can readily deplete its supply of water and it is the only source of water for the sprinkler system.

    B. Gravity tank above the line of sprinklers on top floor is not of sufficient height to provide good pressure at the top floor and this is the area most seriously threatened. The pressure will range from 8 to 10 psi and sprinkler efficiency is greatly increased when sprinkler head pressures are 20 psi or higher.

5. Position: Place aerial platform in front of the exposed building, but about 20 feet from the fire building and along the curb nearest to the exposed building. This position will permit sufficient stream range to accomplish its intended purposes and yet prevent major damage to apparatus when the fire building collapses.

    A. Direct water onto roof of exposed building to prevent · failure of unprotected metal supporting gravity tank.

    B. Cover bulkhead skylight with water stream to prevent further cracking of glass.

    C. Endeavor to create an umbrella of water to cool the seriously exposed shutters.

    D. Protect against spark or brand hazard.

    E. When fire building collapses, darken fire.

6. Duties of ladder company personnel:

    A. Give first consideration to top floor and by walkie-talkie inform the commander of conditions.

    B. Check all other floors for incipient fires and extinguish them with whatever means available.

    C. Ventilate the unexposed sides of the building.

    D. Ventilate the roof when it is safe to do so.

    E. Shut off sprinkler heads operating unnecessarily.

    F. Move paintings, antiques and any other combustible materials away from the wall facing the fire building.

    G. Perform whatever salvage is feasible, especially in respect to art and antiques.

7. A. Their first assignment would be to get a line to the top floor of the exposed building. The diameter of the hose

    depends on the report received from the personnel of Ladder 1.

B. A $1^1/_2$-inch on $1^3/_4$-inch line would be used on the lower floors.

C. If manpower permits, assist the ladder company in its duties. However, if fire conditions are moderate to severe on the top floor, the emphasis should be on this area.

8. Early collapse of the fire building can be predicted. It is a limiting factor that cannot be overcome, therefore it is accepted. So, no companies are assigned to the fire building. In this case, the strategic factor dictates a defensive strategy. Since collapse is predictable, the chief must exercise rigid care so that no personnel or apparatus will be endangered by falling walls.

## TIRE COMPANY FIRE

This exposing fire was possibly the most severe ever to take place in a single building. However, the exposed building was not destroyed nor even appreciably damaged. This phenomenon was due to: (1) fire-resistant construction; (2) the efficient operation of an automatic sprinkler system; (3) the nature of the burning material, rubber tires.

### FIRE BUILDING

The exposing fire building was a four-story reinforced concrete warehouse. It had a partial sprinkler system on the first floor. The structure was 260 X 120 feet and had plate glass windows covering 25 percent of the front or exposing wall. (Figure 6)

### EXPOSED BUILDING

The exposed building was 10 stories high, of reinforced concrete, and was used for manufacturing which involved large amounts of paper and cloth. An 80-foot street separated this

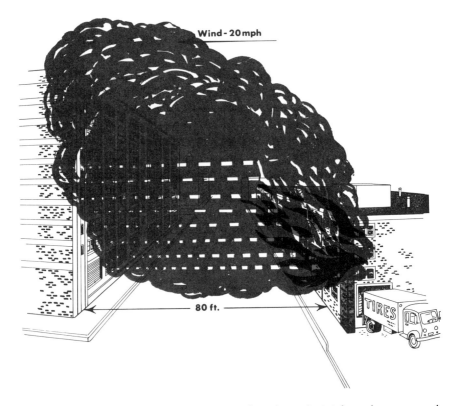

Figure 6.  *Note how lines representing radiant heat diminish as they approach the exposed building. With 80,000 rubber tires and 70,000 inner tubes burning, the smoke and heat on the leeward side prevent firefighters from entering the street.*

building from the exposing fire building. Although the walls were brick, the exposed building had plain glass windows in wooden frames. During the fire, some windows were broken on many floors, but the wooden window frames ignited only on the upper stories. Within the exposure, combustible contents ignited on several of the upper floors. Although 100 sprinkler heads operated to protect the contents, fire proved a threat only in washrooms on the eighth and ninth floors, where recent construction shielded areas from sprinkler protection. These fires and fires in the window frames were extinguished by small hand lines.

At the time of the fire, there were 80,000 rubber tires and 70,000 rubber inner tubes stored to a height of eight feet on each floor of the fire building. The fire consumed the contents of the upper three floors, involving about 2.5 million pounds of rubber.

*FIRE SITUATION*

The wind was blowing at 20 mph from the warehouse to the exposed building. Fire fighters reported that flames shot out great distances toward the manufacturing plant. Attempts at fire control were made from the windward side and from the ends of the warehouse. Positions at the windows on the leeward street could not be maintained because of the intense heat and smoke. Twenty large-caliber streams were used to pour water into window openings. These streams did not appreciably lessen the fire severity at the street side which exposed the manufacturing plant.

Temperatures were high enough to melt corrugated steel elevator doors on the third floor, where the fire started. Fire then spread to the fourth floor via the elevator shaft and later dropped down to involve the second floor. The upper three stories were totally lost before the fire was finally extinguished.

## QUESTIONS

*1. It is estimated that 5 billion Btu radiated from this fire building. Try to envision the smoke and heat situation on the leeward side of the fire. Then discuss the effects of radiant heat on the leeward side.*

2. *The wind was blowing at 20 mph from the fire building toward the exposed building. What effect does wind have on radiated heat conditions?*

3. *Is the radiation problem as severe in the early stages of a fire as it is further along in the development of the fire?*

4. *What was the principal defect in the design or construction of the exposed building?*

5. *Presume you are the chief in charge of this fire. The original response is two 1000-gpm pumping engines, and a 100-foot aerial ladder with a ladder pipe. The manpower response is a total of 15 officers and firemen. There is no life hazard. Other engine and ladder companies will arrive in about 10 minutes. What assignments would you give to each of these companies? Give reasons.*

6. *What are the strategic factors involved in this fire?*

### ANSWERS

1. The smoke from the burning tires and tubes on the leeward side of the fire was dense and black. The radiant heat was absorbed by the opaque smoke. Water possesses little ability to prevent the passage of radiant heat because of its lack of opacity.

Since the smoke was absorbing the radiant heat, the street temperature on the leeward side was intense, and this prevented fire fighters from positioning heavy stream appliances on this street.

2. Radiant heat will travel in all directions regardless of the direction of the wind. Its electromagnetic waves are not affected by wind. Nevertheless, the radiant heat situation will be more severe on the leeward than the windward side.

   In *"The St. Lawrence Burns"* report in the NFPA Quarterly for April 1960, it is stated that "The direction of the wind greatly affected radiation levels, those on the leeward side being the greater, because of the large volume of flame issuing from the windows on this side."

3. Radiation is related to temperatures. It is also related to the area of the fire. As the fire spreads upward to the fourth floor and then drops on the second floor, there is more fire, and consequently more radiant energy.

   In "The St. Lawrence Burns," it is stated that at least 16 minutes elapsed before maximum radiation levels were attained.

   Radiation levels will increase as more tires and tubes become involved, but the temperature will reach only a certain level, perhaps 2000-2500°F. Beyond this, additional fuel results in a longer duration of the exposure problem, not in higher temperatures.

   Therefore, as the fire develops, the radiation problems multiply. The fire originated on the third floor and totally involved this floor. It attained its maximum temperature. In fact, it was so hot that the corrugated steel elevator door melted on the third floor. When this occurred, the fire spread to the fourth floor and dropped to the second floor. With the second, third and fourth floors involved in fire, the amount of radiant energy emitted increased as the area of involvement increased.

4. Although the construction was fireproof and was fully protected by an automatic sprinkler system the building had only plate glass windows in wooden frames. The plate glass

windows broke in many areas, and the wooden frames on the upper floors ignited. If the sprinkler system had been out of service for any reason, the destruction in the exposed building would have been vast. It is evident that a clear space of 80 feet is, in itself, not adequate to protect against radiant and convection heat.

In frame one and two-story residences, building codes often specify a clear space of 10 to 20 feet between buildings. This space does not eliminate the exposure hazard, but assists fire departments in positioning hose lines and laddering.

If the exterior windows in the exposed building had been of metal sash with wire glass the hazard would have been considerably reduced.

5. Engines 1 and 2—Use pumpers to their fullest capacities to feed sprinkler system of exposed building. In a building of this area, there are at least two siamese inlets for the sprinkler system. Then assign personnel to stretch $2^1/_2$-inch lines to the rear of the exposed building. Use $2^1/_2$ X $1^1/_2$-inch gates with $1^1/_2$-inch lines stretched to various floors of the exposed building. Subsequent pumpers are to be used to feed these lines.

*Reasons*

A. Sprinkler systems are generally designed with limited water supplies. At major exposure fires, sprinkler systems, can readily become overtaxed. With 100 heads open, there is a flow of 2000 gpm. The most efficient method of supplying water to an exposed building is through the sprinkler system. Therefore, the two pumpers are used exclusively for this purpose.

B. The manpower of Engines 1 and 2 can quickly stretch large diameter hose to the sprinkler siamese inlets. While awaiting the arrival of additional engine companies, their time can be judiciously employed in stretching of $2^1/_2$ and $1^1/_2$-inch hand lines for use in the exposed building. Even in large area buildings, $1^1/_2$-inch lines are feasible where the buildings are fully protected with automatic sprinkler systems. The sprinkler system will control the intensity of the fire. The line is used for spot fires out of reach of the sprinkler heads, such as under tables.

*Ladder 1*

Position the ladder pipe on the flank of the exposed building so that it can operate its ladder pipe to hit the facing of the exposed building on the upper floors. Later arriving pumpers will feed this ladder pipe.

*Reasons*

Manpower and equipment cannot be initially positioned on the leeward side of the fire because of the severity of the heat. Use the flanks of the fire for positioning heavy stream appliances, until a foothold can be gained on the fire street.

Personnel of the ladder company are to be assigned the following duties in the exposed building:

A. Ventilate unexposed sides of building and roof.

B. Provide access to rear of building for engine companies.

C. If there are any manually started pumps for sprinkler or standpipe systems, get them into operation.

D. Move combustible material away from front windows.

E. Use standpipe lines for major fires, and extinguishers and water pails for incipient fires.

F. Close open windows on fire side of building.

G. Don't shut off floor control or any other shutoff valves in sprinkler system at this stage of the fire. However, use wooden plugs to reduce water damage where the sprinklers are operating but are not protecting any combustible stock. These plugs are cut in the shape of a wedge and are forced into open sprinkler heads. Use whatever other means are available to reduce water damage.

H. The exposure problem will be most serious on the upper floors; this should initially be the area receiving primary consideration. Supplementary companies are to assist Ladder 1 in these duties.

I. Keep officer-in-command informed of conditions.

These actions by Ladder 1 will render the sprinkler system more effective, reduce water damage, and provide information to the officer-in-command of the fire.

6. The strategic factors in this fire are the area of the fire building and the height of the stock. These factors must be accepted, and cannot be overcome.

Therefore, use a defensive strategy, exclusively. Stream penetration into the fire building will be largely ineffective. Concentrate the forces on the protection of the exposed building. Since there is only one exposure in this fire situation and its distance is 80 feet, it can be adequately protected by a sprinkler system, exterior streams flowing water down the facing of the building, plus a number of interior hand lines. In this fire situation, there is no reason for using a great number of companies in the useless maneuver of flowing large-caliber streams into the fire building. This would violate the principle of economy of forces. It would be a waste of manpower, energy and money.

There is sufficient fire loading to keep this fire burning for days. One cannot control the heat generation with exterior streams; therefore, collapse will occur. However, if in the early hours of the fire—say, the first and second hour—it becomes important to gain access to the leeward street, a series of high volume fog streams will have to be used, each positioned in a window of the exposed building. Their purpose would be to engulf the apparatus and fire fighters in an umbrella of water. Of course, all men will wear breathing apparatus because of the heavy smoke condition. No sooner are such assignments made, then plans will have to be made for their early withdrawal.

### *CONCLUSION*

The tire company fire shows that the fire forces cannot take anything for granted at a fire scene. This four-story reinforced concrete, fireproof building was designed and built to protect against fire. It is true that in proper fireproof construction, the probability of collapse is infinitely small, and the same can be said of mill construction. But the unusual does take place. If any building is loaded with a vast amount of combustible stock and then that stock is piled in such a manner as to prevent stream penetration from the exterior, under heavy fire conditions the fire forces will be unable to extinguish the fire.

### PARAGON PAINT FIRE (Figure 7)

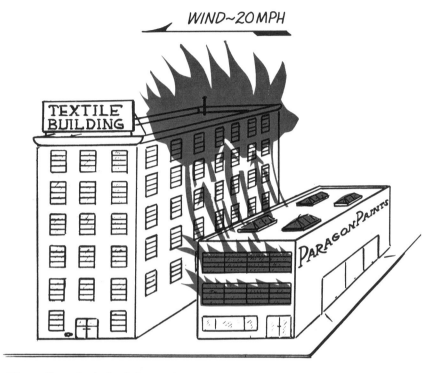

Figure 7. *The ball of flame shown in the drawing represents the ignition of gases too rich to ignite below.*

*FIRE SITUATION*

The fire started in an open vat of lacquer and flashed throughout the second floor with such rapidity that there was not time to activate the manual extinguishing systems. The employees and other occupants ran to the ends of the building and found safe egress to the street. The occupants of the third floor were equally fortunate.

The fire spread by auto-exposure to the third floor. By the time the fire companies arrive, the second and third floors are fully involved in fire, the roof skylights have cracked, and a 20-mile wind is blowing the fire toward exposed building.

### CONSTRUCTION

The fire building is of non-fireproof construction with cast-iron columns supporting steel girders. The metal structural members are unprotected. The building is 40 × 100 feet and is three stories high. The stairways are at opposite ends of the building and are enclosed in fireproof partitions. Their doors are self-closing fire doors. The roof deck is wood, pierced by four skylights.

### OCCUPANCY

The building is occupied by one tenant, and used for the manufacture of paints, varnishes and lacquers.

### AUXILIARY APPLIANCES

There is an assortment of water, foam and $CO_2$ extinguishers spaced at 50-foot intervals on all of the floors. Open vats used for mixing are protected by manually-operated foam extinguishing systems.

### EXPOSED BUILDING

An exposed building is 40 × 100 feet and six stories high. It is of fire-proof construction, but the exterior windows are of wood sash with ordinary glass. The standpipe system has two street siamese connections. The system is fed from two distinct street mains, which supply a suction tank from which a stationary 1000-gpm manually started pump sunctions the water. The occupancy is largely devoted to showrooms for ladies' apparel.

Two aerial ladder companies with ladder pipes and three engine companies respond to the fire. Each company is manned by five men.

1. *Why would the first two ladder pipe streams be directed against the exposed building from opposite directions with the water flowing down the facing of the building?*

2. *Why would a water curtain developed between the two buildings and not touching either one of them be somewhat inefficient?*

3. *What effect do rates of water flow and nozzle pressures have on the absorption of radiant heat?*

4. *Why is the exposure hazard much greater on the fourth, fifth and sixth floors than on the lower floors?*

5. *Why is it essential that exterior heavy streams be in operation before committing companies to the interior of the fireproof building?*

*6. What are the strategic factors involved in this fire?*

*ANSWERS*

1. The flame front will have considerable height and width. Since the distance between the two buildings is only 30 feet, the radiation hazard can be characterized as an area source rather than a point source. Therefore, the radiant heat as it travels this distance will diminish, but the decrease will be negligible.

The fire building will collapse. Unprotected metals under load-bearing conditions cannot withstand the ravages of a massive fire. Radiant heat will then change from an area source to a line course. The radiant heat will diminish inversely with the distance. Mathematically it can be stated that the radiant heat at the exposure will be $1/30$ of its intensity at the fire building.

The convection currents will lose some of their heat intensity as they flow across the 30-foot distance, but the convection currents will also rise and some will pillar skyward, thereby not contributing to the exposure problem.

At the fire scene, in the early stages of fire fighting, the officer in charge of the fire is limited by equipment and manpower. His principal problem is to use water most judiciously. To direct streams into the fire building would be calamitous. The water would have little effect upon the fire because of its limited quantity. The amount of heat units at the exposure would be much less than at the fire building.

Therefore, it will be much more effective to direct the ladder pipe streams against the exposed wall, letting the water flow down the facing of the building, extinguishing or darkening the fire in the window frames and cooling the glass windows in an endeavor to keep them intact. If the heat breaks the glass windows, radiant and convection heat will ignite com-

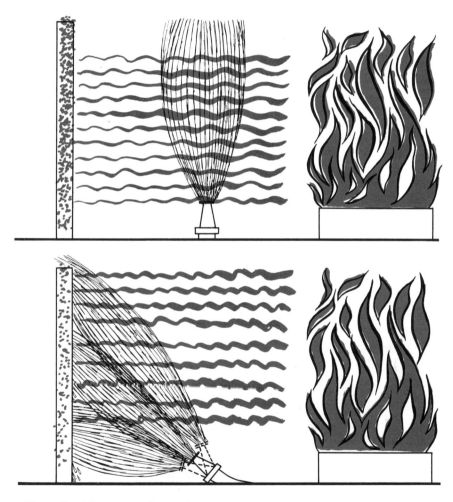

Figure 8.   *The stream directed between the fire and the sheet metal (exposure) was between one-quarter and one-third as effective in absorbing radiant heat as the stream directed against the sheet metal. Water has little opacity, but when directed against an exposure it will absorb significant amounts of heat units.*

bustible contents inside the exposed building. These exterior streams will not offer full protection to the exposure, but they will make it much easier for companies to operate inside the exposure.

### 2. Opacity and Reflectivity

Tests conducted by Underwriters' Laboratories, Inc., with water fog to provide exposure protection to a sheet metal surface from an exposing gasoline fire indicated that when a fog was applied so as to provide a thin film of water over the sheet metal, the temperature of the metal was held to limits adequate to protect it against significant damage. This was not true, however, when the water fog was directed so that it did not contact the sheet metal but provided only a water curtain between the metal and the exposing fire. In this latter case, temperatures on the metal were as much as three to four times greater than when the water flowed over the metal.

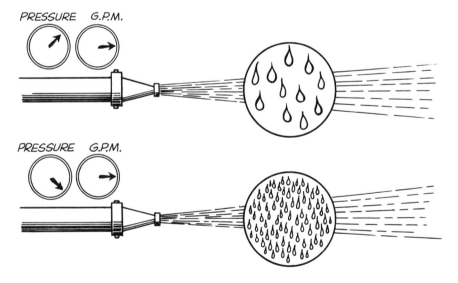

Figure 9. *With the same flow, the smaller droplets, produced by higher pressure, will absorb more radiant heat.*

3. In Fire Technology (May, 1965), it is stated that the transmission of heat falls as the rate of flow of water increases. Further, heat transmission falls as water pressure increases even when the rate of flow does not change because the higher pressure tends to produce smaller drops. (Figure 9)

This indicates the need for large master streams and high nozzle pressures. One of the present developments throughout the United States is an improvement in master stream appliances. These super streams discharge 3000-3500 gpm or more; however, for effectiveness the super streams should be directed against exposed buildings rather than between buildings. There is no doubt of the effectiveness of large calibre and super streams at massive fire situations.

4. A. Radiation will expose the second and third floors, but both radiation and convection will intensify exposure on upper floors.
   B. Over-roof exposure augmented by a strong wind will drive convection currents into the upper floors.
   C. In the fire building, the paints will rapidly decompose, generating great quantities of flammable gases. There will be inadequate oxygen for all of these gases to form into flammable mixtures within the paint factory. This will result in columns of hot unburned gases escaping through window and roof opernings. They will travel upward and with the wind until they reach sufficient oxygen. Then, bursting into flames, they will increase the radiation and convection intensities at the upper levels of the exposed building and the flames themselves may impinge upon the exposed wall or enter the building.

5. Unless exterior heavy streams are in operation before putting companies inside the fireproof building, as soon as the companies extinguish fire, the convection heat will reignite the combustibles.

6. The strategic factors are the collapse of fire building, which dictates a defensive strategy, and the construction of the exposed building. Since the exposed building is fireproof,

companies can be assigned within the building, which means that this building can be properly defended. If the building was non-fireproof with open stairways, the jeopary to the firemen's lives would be severe and unwarranted. The loss of the building would have to be conceded, since this strategic factor could not be overcome.

## Chapter 7

# *Indirect Method of Attack*

The present chapter discusses the indirect method of attack and the danger of rear yards in loft areas.

In the Navy fire fighting schools during World War II, one of the most spectacular fires demonstrated was a simulated boiler room fully involved in fire. When most of the openings were closed, the fire entered the third phase, and it was spectacularly extinguished by the indirect method of attack. Fog was introduced from the roof area and as the small droplets of water impinged on the highly heated metal, the resulting steam instantly smothered the fire. The spectators would gasp at the effectiveness of this method of extinguishment.

The author was in command of the fire fighting school at Pearl Harbor during a phase of World War II and he resolved that if ever the opportunity arose, whereby he could use this method of attack, and save the firefighters the punishment of an interior attack, he would not hesitate to adopt it. Although he responded to thousands of major fires, he was able to employ the indirect method of attack on only a limited number of fires. The extinguishment, again, was spectacular.

Seldom are conditions favorable for this method of attack. The fire strategist, however, should be well acquainted with the method, for its success under the proper conditions is phenomenal.

There are two strategic factors for any fire where the indirect method of attack can be utilized. They are:—

(1) No person is within the building.

(2) Fire has entered the third or smoldering phase.

## APEX ARTIFICIAL FLOWERS FIRE (Figure1)

*CONSTRUCTION*

The building is an old-type loft, non-fireproof, 40 X 90 feet and four stories high. It is on a street of similar structures. The stairs are enclosed in fire-resistant partitions with a self-closing fire door leading to each of the occupancies. A fire escape is in the rear. Windows are in the front and rear of the building. Since the buildings are continguous, the side walls are unpierced.

*OCCUPANCY*

The building is used throughout for manufacturing artificial flowers.

*EXPOSED BUILDING*

The exposed building in the rear is similar to the fire building in construction, area, and height. Each floor has one occupancy for either the manufacture of dresses, handbags, gloves, or bathrobes or as a showroom for these products. The second and fourth floor rear windows are of ordinary glass. On the first and third floors, the windows are protected by metal shutters.

*FIRE SITUATION*

The fire is at 3 p.m. Sunday. The businesses have been closed since 5 p.m. Friday. The neighborhood is virtually deserted on weekends. A police car notices a column of smoke from about

Figure 1. *Conventional fire fighting tactics will destroy this structure. This is an ideal situation for the Indirect Method of Attack.*

four blocks away. On investigation, the patrolman finds the fire and immediately sends in an alarm.

*RESPONSE*

Two engine companies and one aerial ladder company, each manned by an officer and five firemen, respond. The deputy chief, while inspecting the district, spots this column of smoke and is the first to arrive at the scene. While awaiting the arrival of companies, the chief is making quick size-up notes:

A. Smoke is pushing out of all windows, front and rear, and a cloud of smoke is engulfing the building.

B. The first floor has a glow of flame. No other flame is visible.

*QUESTIONS*

*1. Do not ventilate or open the building in any manner whatsoever until companies have adequately protected the exposures. What are the reasons for this?*

*2. What orders are issued to the engine and ladder companies?*

*3. In the congested loft areas of many major cities, the rear of the fire building frequently is the channel for major fire extension. Explain.*

*4. It is a scientific truth that water is the most effective heat-absorbing extinguishant that can be used. Explain the efficiency of water in relation to the indirect method of attack.*

*5. This fire is ideal for the indirect method of attack. Why?*

*6. Lloyd Layman, in his book, "Attacking and Extinguishing Interior Fires," advocated the indirect method of attack as the primary strategy in fire fighting. Discuss this.*

7. *Outline the manner of executing the indirect method of attack.*

1. Here we have the components of a back draft. The thunderous effects of a smoke explosion can cause deaths of fire fighters, demolition of the fire building, and major fire extension to adjoining buildings. To understand the risks that confront the fire officer, a knowledge of the three phases of fire development is a prerequisite. The progress of fire involving ordinary combustible materials within the usual closed building can be classified, as follows:

*First Phase*
This might be called the incipient phase. Where there is slow fuel consumption, limited heat generation and production of considerable smoke, there is a free supply of air surrounding the fire and little danger of a back draft.

*Second Phase*
This is the period of major flame production. The heat generated creates strong convection currents which carry hot combustion products upward and throughout the fire area. Windows sometimes fail from the effects of the heat, and a fresh supply of air is admitted to support additional flame production and further fire extension. There is little danger of a back draft at this stage.

*Third Phase*
When the fire continues to burn for a time without venting

itself to the outer air, it enters the third, or smoldering phase. Under these conditions, oxygen content of the available air is used up quickly, and since comparatively little air seeps in from outside, the flames begin to subside as the available oxygen in the area drops below 15 percent. There is a transfer of heat from the interior atmosphere to the contents and structure of the building. The combustible materials undergo a process of destructive distillation, emitting great quantities of combustible gases. Many of the combustibles within the space are in a state of readiness and need only additional oxygen to support rapid combustion. A fire in this pahse has all the basic factors for a smoke explosion.

If fire fighting procedures are well coordinated, a back draft may be prevented. But the situation is so delicate and pregnant with so much danger, that no unnecessary risks should be taken.

When fighting fires in the first and second phases, speed of action is important.

In the third phase, caution is the keynote to the development of fire strategy. The fire has insufficient oxygen to support rapid flaming combustion. The fire is in the smoldering stage. This is a great advantage which you can retain as long as doors, windows and roof openings remain intact. It provides the chief with time to get additional companies to the scene, protect exposures and develop a coordinated attack.

2. Operate in the rear of the exposed building, exposure 3.

*Engine Companies:*
Stretch 2$^1$/$_2$-inch lines up the interior stairs of exposure 3 to second and fourth floors, lines to be taken to the rear of building to cover yard. Charge all lines and stand by.

*Ladder Companies*—operate in exposure 3
1. Perform necessary forcible entry.
2. Check and close shutters at rear of building and remove any combustible stock close to shutters.
3. Aerial to roof and vent roof. Take roof rope and hose roller to roof to expedite further stretching of hose lines.
4. Ventilate other floors except for windows on rear wall.

3. *Explanation:*

The front of a fire building gets immediate and adequate protection, then the chief will invariably assign companies to the adjoining exposures. This is rather a natural sequence since these buildings are in immediate view of the chief standing in front of the fire building.

In tenement sections, where the rear yards are often 40 feet deep and shafts are contiguous to the buildings, this is proper procedure. But in congested loft areas of cities, it is the rear of the fire building that frequently provides the channel for great fire extension because there may be only 20 feet or less separating the backs of buildings.

Where such conditions exist and the chief arrives to find the first-alarm companies in front of the fire building, it is imperative that the second-alarm companies be ordered to protect the rear of the fire building.

There are numerous locations in many of our cities where old and new-type buildings are adjacent to each other. In such cases, the old buildings present a constant exposure threat to the new buildings. The records are replete with exposure fires causing substantial losses to new buildings, even though they were of fireproof construction and protected with wire-glass windows. In some instances, they had full automatic sprinkler system protection.

*Fire at 230 W. 58th Street* (Figure 2)

The New York City building in which the fire originated was of ordinary brick construction. It was built in the form of an L with the rear portion extending across the rear of 228 W. 58th St., which was occupied by a dealer in rubber specialties.

When the first engine company arrived, the street was so filled with dense black smoke that it was difficult to locate hydrants. As the companies started toward the building, a burst of flame from 230 W. 58th St. rolled across the street. The fire had practically complete possession of the fire building and was spreading to 228 and 232 W. 58th St.

The 12th floor of 1780–2 Broadway was completely gutted.

This latter building was of fireproof construction and completely protected by an automatic sprinkler system with good sources of water supply. The fire department had connected

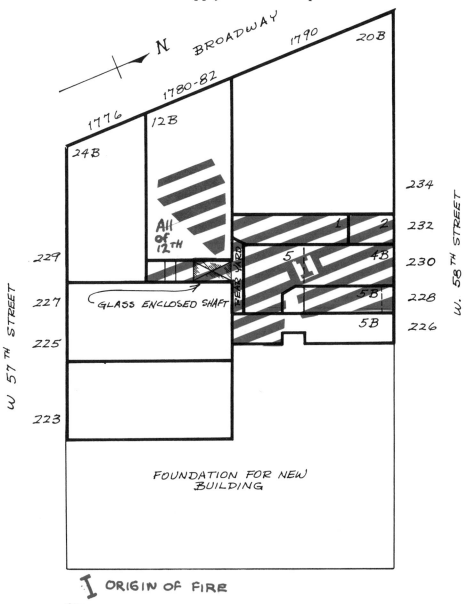

**Figure 2.** *Plan view of fire at 230 West 58th Street, New York City.*

two 1000-gpm pumpers to the street siameses to augment the sprinkler water supply system. But since there was a glass-enclosed elevator shaft at the rear of this building, the fire broke through the wire-glass enclosure and exposed all 12 floors simultaneously. The sprinkler system was evidently overtaxed and although it did a favorable job in protecting the lower floors, the 12th floor was ravaged by fire.

When a chief arrives at these fire situations, he has more problems than companies. With the best means of communication, it will take a minimum of 15 minutes to accumulate all the facts necessary for the development of a proper fire strategy. But in this time, the fire is extending. Therefore, a fire chief must take immediate action based upon a visual picture of the fire and his previous fire experience.

The principle expounded here is that at this type fire situation, the chief should give immediate attention to the rear of the fire building. This action is taken before he has an overall view of the fire situation. It is based on the fact that rear yards in loft sections have narrow depths and that there are many windows or openings bordering on these yards. Furthermore, it takes longer to position lines in the rear than in the front of a fire building. If the yard is narrow, the building materials are rapidly heated, and the hotter the materials become, the greater will be the velocity of the flow of gases up this flue. This will accelerate burning on the fire floor and can cause extension of the fire to all buildings bordering the yard.

4. A. It is in the process of vaporization that water exerts its maximum cooling action:
    1. One gallon of water absorbs about 1250 Btu when its temperature rises from 62 to 212 degrees Fahrenheit.
    2. It absorbs 8080 Btu just during vaporization.
    (Note: Wood produces about 8000 Btu per pound.)
    3. Thus, it takes 9,330 Btu to convert an entire gallon of water at 62° F into steam.
  B. Steam expands about 1600 times.
  C. One gallon of water will generate approximately 223 cubic

feet of steam. If the application of water is only 90 percent efficient, one gallon of water will produce about 200 cubic feet of steam. The desirable objective is to increase the surface area of the water and convert as much of it to steam as possible. This depends upon the fineness with which the water is delivered to the fire area in the form of fog.

D. Based upon 90 percent efficiency, 125 gallons of water will absorb approximately one million Btu and produce about 25,000 cubic feet of steam. Condensing steam is visible and it contains insufficient heat to cause physical injury. It is not toxic, but it restricts visibility.

5. The fire has been burning and smoldering since Friday evening. It has not vented itself. The smoke engulfing the building, the hot glass, and the limited fire glow are indicative of a third phase fire. Most importantly, there is no life hazard. Opening the roof or upper floor will create an upward draft and the full involvement of the building. Opening the first floor before upper level ventillation is provided will likely create a back draft. Fire probably started on the first floor. The windows can easily be pierced for the operation of the fog stream.

6. Most structural fires occur in occupied buildings. The first consideration here must be the saving of life. This necessitates a direct attack. As the lines are being moved into the building between the fire and the occupants, the laddermen are searching and evacuating endangered areas.

As fire develops, heat becomes intense and of sufficient magnitude to cause cracking and failure of plain glass windows. If a fire has broken through to the exterior by means of the roof or a number of window openings, steam generated by an indirect attack will readily dissipate through these openings because of its lightness. It will thereby lose its blanketing effect, which is an essential phase of the method. The indirect method is one of the strategies in fire fighting. It is not utopian. When it has application, it is very effective. The fire outlined in this case was an actual situation. The

2¹/₂-inch fog lines operated simultaneously for two minutes. The fire was out.

7. A. Close as many intake air openings as possible.
   B. Make only those openings necessary to insert nozzles.
   C. Use fog streams.
   D. The initial attack should be made within the area of major involvement, especially at the upper levels of rooms, where temperatures are highest.
   E. The rapid generation of steam within a confined space creates a violent atmospheric disturbance within the space.
   F. This will cause steam and water particles to spread beyond the immediate area of application, thereby creating cooling action throughout the atmospheric area.
   G. This action will continue until the atmospheric temperature is approximately 212° F. The steam will then condense and in turn will be replaced by cool air from the outside.
   H. A high heat concentration within a closely confined space provides the most advantageous conditions.
   I. Indirect application and atmospheric displacement will occur effectively only on and above the floor where the attack is made.
   J. The progress of an indirect attack can be estimated readily by observing the volume of smoke and condensing steam coming from a building during the attack. Displacement of the interior atmosphere starts immediately following the injection of water particles and continues in the following sequence:
      (1) Violent expulsion of smoke.
      (2) A mixture of smoke and condensing steam.
      (3) Condensing steam and little smoke.
   K. Injection of water particles should continue without interruption until the volume of condensing steam coming from the building has decreased to a major degree.
   L. If an indirect attack has been executed in the proper manner, the following conditions can be anticipated:
      a. Residual heat will be low enough for personnel to enter and operate inside the building. Conventional methods

of ventilation may be used to lower the humidity and to further reduce the temperature.

b. Some smoke and condensing steam may be present at upper levels but usually of insufficient density to interfere with visibility.

c. Oxygen content will be normal.

d. Small spot fires and deep-seated smoldering may be found.

M. When the interior temperature has been sufficiently reduced, firemen should enter and operate inside the building.

*Chapter 8*

# Major Nursing Home Fire

A reader of Fire Engineering, Fire Command!, Fire Journal or any other fire periodical is appalled at the great loss of life in wood frame nursing home fires. It would appear that we are out "to get" the elderly and the incapacitated. Certainly, all of these buildings should be fully protected by an automatic sprinkler system. However, since that is not the case, the chief had better preplan his forces for the catastrophic fire.

There is generally limited manpower in the initial response to large nursing home fires. The concept which should guide the chief in assigning the meager number of companies present is to take whatever action will help the greatest number of people. This principle is well illustrated in the following fire situation and should help guide the chief in pre-fire planning for nursing homes.

**FIRE SITUATION— (Figure 1)**

At 2:30 p.m., a major fire originated on the first floor of a nursing home annex. By the time the fire department reached

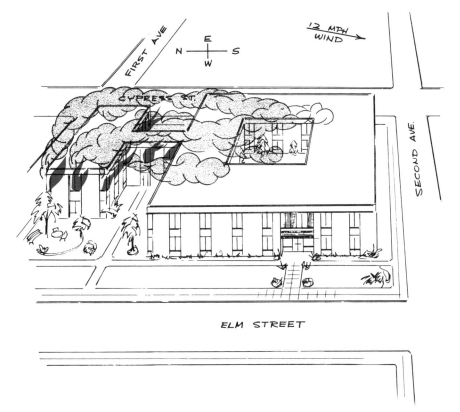

Figure 1. *This an occupied nursing home with a large body of fire in the smaller or annex part of the building. Fire threatens the main building.*

the scene, the fire had extended laterally on the first floor and, via open stairs, had spread throughout the second floor. Smoke and flame were pushing toward the corridors of the main building and fire was visible from many second floor annex windows. There were 149 tenants in the nursing home—30 of them in the annex.

Three engine and two aerial ladder companies responded with five men and an officer for each unit.

Engine 1 hooked up large suction to hydrant 1 and stretched a 2¹/₂-inch line to the main building first floor, to protect it against extension via the connecting corridor.

Engine 2 hooked up large suction to hydrant 2 and stretched a 2¹/₂-inch line to the second floor of the main building to cover extension via the corridor.

Engine 3 hooked up to hydrant 3, using its large suction, and stretched a 2¹/₂-inch line into the annex. This company successfully extinguished fire on the first floor and endeavored to move up the stairs to cope with the fire on the second floor.

*QUESTIONS*

*1. Discuss strategy in respect to this fire and the reasons for positioning the lines of Engine 1 and Engine 2.*

*2. Why is it so important for the engine companies to use large suction for their connection to hydrants?*

*3. Exterior streams should be in operation as soon as practicable. Why?*

*4. Aerial Ladder 1 was assigned to the annex. What would be its principal activities?*

*5. Aerial Ladder 2 was assigned to the main building to perform functions similar to those of Ladder 1. Enumerate any additional activities that should be performed by this company.*

6. *Is the chief justified in positioning his forces within the annex? Explain.*

7. *Fire departments throughout the country specialize in their work activities at fires so that engine and ladder companies have distinct duties. In the nursing home fire, all the men in the engine company were used in stretching hose and confining and extinguishing fire. The ladder companies had only 10 men, and certainly more men than this were needed to assist and rescue the patients. Doesn't this assignment of forces violate the principle that primary consideration should be given to saving life?*

*8. Should Ladder 2 evacuate the main building?*

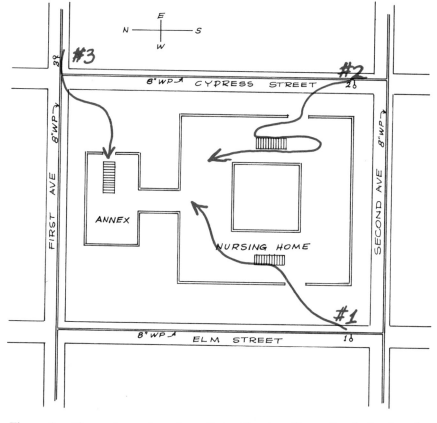

Figure 2. *Shown is a plan view of the Nursing Home fire indicating the correct positioning of hose lines #1, #2 and #3.*

1. The strategic factor in this fire is that originally the chief has a limited number of companies and manpower. If he had unlimited manpower, his strategy would be offensive. However, in this situation he must apply his forces to save the greatest number of people. This leads to a defensive strategy in respect to the original assignment of companies and to an offensive strategy when the fire is cut off in the main building. The strategy, therefore, is defensive-offensive.

   Since there are 30 persons in the annex and 119 in the main building, and smoke and flames are pushing toward the connecting corridor, the first lines must be used to cut off this extension and to push the flames and smoke back from the corridor toward the annex building. (Figure 2)

2. The fire situation warrants the immediate transmittal of greater alarms. Plan at this stage for incoming companies. There are three hydrants connected to an 8-inch main in the immediate vicinity of the nursing home. By insisting that the first three engine companies use their large suction hose, it will facilitate the stretching for subsequent arriving companies. If the pumpers are of 1000-gpm capacity or greater, three or four major lines can be supplied by each pumper.

   The old concept, whereby the chief in command merely ordered the officers of the incoming engines to stretch to a designated position without specifying from where to stretch, was usually highly inefficient. At greater alarm fires, it was not unusual to see men connecting to pumpers two or three blocks from the fire building.

   There is much better planning at fire situations today. The chiefs try to use to their fullest capacities, the pumpers closest to the fire.

   With the advent of large diameter hose, (4, 4½, 5 and even 6-inch) a new evolution has been established in firemanics, whereby the large diameter hose feeds a portable hydrant situated near the fire building. These portable hydrants have three to six outlets. This evolution facilitates the stretching of lines by incoming companies. The lines go into operation more quickly, friction losses are less and streams are more effective, especially master streams.

Another innovation since the introduction of gated inlets is the positioning of a pumper in front of the fire building. Large diameter supply hose is connected to gated suction inlets and incoming companies then can readily stretch lines from this conveniently located pumper.

Other important advantages accrue from this inline pumping evolution. Since the pumper is near the fire building, all its equipment is readily available, such as hose, nozzles, master stream appliances, breathing apparatus and all sorts of minor equipment. In addition, the pump operator is more cognizant of the fire operation and can better adapt to changes in operation.

Manpower is always in short supply in the early stages of fighting major alarms. It is a resource that should be expended judiciously. Short stretches mean less fatigue to men, water into the critical areas of the fire faster, and many times, the elimination of the need to send an additional alarm.

3. Exterior streams are needed to cover the outside rescues and to prevent the spread of fire from the annex to the main building through windows. These exterior streams should not be directed into the building to extinguish fire. Directing exterior streams inside can easily drive the fire into the corridors or toward trapped patients. As an exterior stream penetrates the building, it will force the high heat currents and flame at the ceiling level rearward. There is the natural tendency, and the desire to extinguish fire wherever it appears, but such actions will jeopardize rather than save life.

4. Aerial Ladder 1, working in the annex, should:
   A. Raise portable ladders to the exterior of the building in accordance with the needs of the situation and make rescues.
   B. Raise aerial to roof and attempt to open up over all vertical arteries, cut roof to increase ventilation and open cockloft area. If feasible, cut roof over corridor to channel fire.

   C. Under the protection of the line from Engine 3, search
      and evacuate the annex first floor.
   D  Check all sides of the annex for jumpers and persons
      needing assistance.
   E. Shut off all public utilities at the street level.
   F. Provide portable lights on the first floor of the annex to
      expedite search and fire extinguishment.
   G. Where necessary, open ceilings and side partitions.
   H. Assist doctors and ambulance corps members in setting
      up a first aid station and a morgue.
   I. Remove the dead in accordance with established proce-
      dures.
   J. Assist Engine 3 in moving line to second floor of annex
      and under the protection of the stream, remove trapped
      patients.
   K. There are more functions to be performed than personnel,
      so this company will have to be reinforced with additional
      personnel responding on greater alarms or mutual aid
      response. In the interim, do those things first that will
      help the greatest number of people.

5. Aerial Ladder 2, working in the main building, should:
   A. Pull ceilings on first and second floors near corridor to
      annex to expose fire for engine company operations.
      Close fire doors where feasible.
   B. Search interior courtyard for people trapped and for
      jumpers.
   C. Close windows exposed to the annex.
6. Assigning fire fighters to the interior of the annex is risky.
   This is an old building; the fire is vast. The chief certainly
   cannot foretell what will occur. There may be structural
   failure. However, humans are trapped inside the building.
   Therefore risks must be taken by fire fighters until all possible
   rescues have been made. Operations should be conducted
   with a view to minimizing the risks to members as far as is
   consistent with the goal of rescuing endangered persons.

7. The primary purpose of engine operations at this fire is to
   save life, not the buildings. One of the most effective ways to
   save life is to get water on the fire as quickly as possible. In

the annex, the exterior and interior streams make it possible for the ladder personnel to make their rescues. The streams in the main building are to confine the fire to ensure the safety of the residents.

If all the engine company personnel devoted themselves to laddering the buildings and to search and evacuation, the toll of dead would be much greater. In rare situations, the engine company personnel may use a scaling ladder or a *life net* to affect a rescue. This usually happens where the danger is imminent and the ladder personnel have not yet arrived on the scene. Generally, this specialization or division of work functions favorably.

8. This situation is replete with dangers. Presume the officer of Ladder 2 personally asks the chief in charge of the fire if he should evacuate the building. Imagine the flashes of thoughts within the mind of the chief. "Will the fire run the ceiling spaces and suddenly jeopardize the entire building?" Suppose he does not evacuate and the life loss is great. Because of these pressing possibilities, most chiefs play it safe and evacuate.

The principle which prevails in this situation is to carry out rescue operations in the safest possible manner. Suppose, for example, that there is a smoldering fire in a large sawdust bin in the cellar of another nursing home. Although the fire is of limited extent, there are great clouds of smoke and *toxic* gases permeating the building. To remove the elderly, infirm, sick and, in some cases, non-ambulatory patients, would be tragic. It constitutes an unnecessary risk. The safest method of rescue would be to thoroughly ventilate the building and extinguish the fire.

To further clarify the point, presume there is a fire in a single room on an upper floor of a hotel. There is a long corridor with many rooms opening on the corridor. The door to the fire room is open and the smoke and heat within the corridor jeopardize the hotel tenants sleeping in the bordering rooms. Where experience indicates that the fire can be readily controlled, it is better strategy to attack the fire and examine the bordering rooms. If primary consideration is given to evacuation, the corridors and stairs will be crowded with escaping people, and fire fighters will be impeded in stretching and advancing hose lines. The fire will gain in momentum and threaten the lives of many people. The surest method of protecting the safety of the people is a quick stretch and extinguishment of the fire.

The strategy is determined upon weighing the factors. If the fire can be confined to the annex by the cutoff lines at the corridors, then this is the best method to insure the safety of the patients in the main building.

The most spectacular method of rescue is not always the most practical from the standpoint of safety. Where removal is necessary give priority in the following order when possible:

A. Stairs
B. Fire escape
C. Elevating platforms
D. Aerial ladders
E. Portable ladders
F. Roof rope and life belt
G. Life net

*CONCLUSION:*

Where the life situation is serious and extensive, and the fire chief is ordering preference for some over others, his position is not enviable since he is playing the role of God. But if he can establish the order of activity from established principles, then the preference becomes impersonal. The principles the author used throughout many years of his career are as follows:

1. A human life is much more valuable than any fire building.
2. Get water on the fire as quickly as possible, for by diminishing the heat and flame, rescue operations can proceed more expeditiously.
3. In rescue operations, give priority to the people in the most imminent danger.

4. However, when forces are limited and the fire situation is extensive, rescue operations are concentrated on performing those acts which will help the greatest number of people.
5. Rescue operations must proceed in the safest possible manner.
6. When necessary, jeopardize your fire fighting forces to save life, but do not unnecessarily jeopardize your forces to save property.
7. Exterior streams are unwarranted where they may drive fire, heat or toxic gases in the direction of tenants or firemen.
8. After being informed by a subordinate that the building has been searched and evacuated, conduct another search with a different team of firefighters.

*Chapter 9*

# Fire in College Building

There are many college buildings in our cities and communities. If not a college, then high school or grade school buildings of similar type construction are found. The fires in these edifices are not too frequent, but nevertheless, serious fire situations do occur. The fire described in this case study requires a much different approach from the day-in, day-out type of fire fighting. That is why it is so important for the chief to plan for this eventuality. The principal objective in this fire is to assist the chiefs and other officers in planning for the safety features which must be given consideration if the fire is to be fought without injury or deaths to the fire personnel.

Tactical alternatives are discussed in the handling of this fire situation. There are, to be sure, many additional alternatives. But to consider them all would make the case study far too lengthy and actually would detract from its principal objective, which is a discussion of safety procedures in sound fireproof structures.

## DESCRIPTION OF BUILDING

This was a modern, fireproof, three-story college building, very large in area, and air-conditioned throughout.

On the Cypress Street side of building, there were two exceptionally large enclosed stairways. Heavy thermopane glass enclosed one of the exterior walls of the stair shaft. The exterior walls were made of 36-inch granite blocks. The floors of the building were 8-inch reinforced concrete, and the piping for all the utilities was hung from the underside of these floors.

The building was on a slope, with the Rose Street side at street level and the Cypress Street side at basement level. The only windows on the basement-first floor level were on the Cypress Street side, and they were only partial upper windows, since most of the floor was below street level.

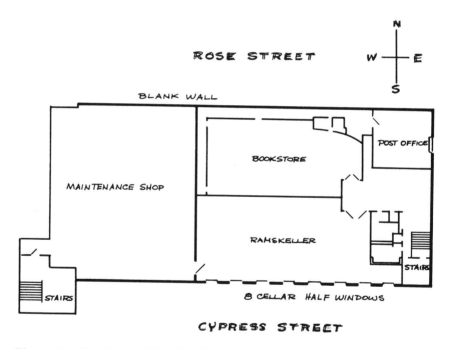

Figure 1. *The inaccessible, hot fire was difficult to ventilate. Construction features would contain the fire but safety of firemen posed a serious problem.*

**BOOK STORE**

The book store was completely separated from the rest of the area by concrete block partitions to the ceiling. Its occupancy consisted of books, and PX-type merchandise. The books were on shelving that extended around the perimeter of the store to the ceiling. The rest of the merchandise was stored in supermarket fashion—although the shelving was only 3-feet high. The book store was 55 X 125 feet.

### "RAMSKELLER"

A hall, called the "Ramskeller" was used for catering, dances and other social events. There were no openings from this hall to any other part of the building, except for some adjoining rooms used for kitchen and refrigeration purposes. There was access to the Ramskeller from both stairways.

### FIRE SITUATION

The fire was extensive throughout the book store, but was confined to that area. However, the air-conditioning system must have been in operation, for smoke and heat were intense in the Ramskeller, and the upper two floors were permeated with dense smoke with some heat. The shutoff for the air-conditioning system was located only after the fire was under control. The doors to the Ramskeller were closed when fire department units arrived.

### WATER SUPPLY

There was a yard hydrant system throughout the campus with good spacing of hydrants and adequate water supply. the yard hydrant system was connected on two different city streets to a 20-inch water main.

### WEATHER

The temperature was in the 60s and the day was very humid.

Two 2½-inch lines were stretched down the east stairs to the entrance of the book store. The men were all wearing self-contained breathing apparatus. The heat was of such intensity that these lines never moved more than 20 feet inside the book store.

The windows on the Cypress Street side were broken and, although some smoke and heat were exhausted, the conditions in the basement did not noticeably improve.

The personnel of a ladder company descended the west stairway and entered the Ramskeller. A report reached the officer in command that two members had become separated from the unit and their whereabouts were unknown. The smoke density, heat, large area, and lack of visibility made the search slow and difficult. But they were found and safely removed to the street. At this time, no more personnel were permitted in this area. The large fire doors of the Ramskeller adjoining the book store were ordered to be kept closed.

Another fireman was found practically in a state of panic in the cul-de-sac between the post office and the book store. Fortunately he was found and safely removed to the street.

Ladder men were assigned to the second and third floors and, with screwdrivers, were able to open all the windows and practically clear these floors of smoke and heat. The air-conditioning controls were later found to be in a small locked room on the third floor.

The high-expansion foam unit was out of service at the time of this fire.

*A. Evaluate and comment on each of the following:*
   *1.  Shut off the gas feed to the building.*

   *2.  Pull the main electrical switch, since water is causing arcing of an exposed wire.*

   *3.  Use 2½-inch fog streams to sweep the book store and the generated steam will extinguish the fire.*

4. Cut holes in the 8-inch reinforced concrete first floor for insertion of distributors and cellar pipes.

*B. Answer the following questions, giving reasons.*

5. Why would firemen lose their confidence in fighting this type fire?

6. What precautions would you take in respect to safety of personnel operating lines in the book store?

7.  *How much heat can men tolerate and for what period of time? Or, in different words, how frequently would you provide relief for the firemen working in this highly heated atmosphere?*

8.  *After an hour, the two 2½-inch lines in the book store advanced no more than 20 feet, although the depth of the store was 125 feet. The fire continued to burn vigorously, the companies were being relieved frequently, but there was no further advancement. What is your next move in respect to extinguishment?*

9. *Presume the action taken in 8 does not noticeably improve the situation. The chief then orders that the thermal glass enclosing one side of the east stairway be completely broken, using the aerial ladder to ram the glass loose from its framework. This action considerably increased the velocity of the flow of the gases toward the east stairway. The Ramskeller doors near the book store were then opened. The density of smoke and intensity of heat diminished rapidly. What action could now be taken to complete the extinguishment of this fire?*

*ANSWERS*

A. 1.  This is a good procedure. It requires only one man and is easily performed. Most fire departments carry a special wrench to close gas valves. There are various locations for shutoffs, but the usual one is a box sunk in the sidewalk in front of building near the curb.

2.  This would be a poor procedure. You shut down the electrical system only when conditions force you to take such action. An arcing wire is not such a condition.

Firemen operate more safely and effectively in an illuminated situation. As the upper floors are being ventilated, lights will improve the working conditions. The electrical shutdown will stall elevators, necessitating checking for trapped personnel. In some high-rise structures, there are blind elevator shafts, i.e., from the 1st to the 40th floor, there may not be any elevator doors to the floors. Imagine the problems of checking these shafts!

Pulling the main electrical switch is a matter to be given the most profound consideration. Will it multiply or diminish the problems?

If the fire is in one of the major transformers or the generating plant, then the system may have to be deactivated. Before taking such action, however, all tenants must be evacuated and elevators checked and positioned at the first floor level.

3. This would be a poor procedure. Since there is no ventilation in the direction in which fire and heat are being pushed, the use of fog is too hazardous. A fog stream operates like a fan. It creates a high-pressure zone in front of you and a low-pressure zone at the nozzle. The flame and heat will bounce off the blank walls and flow from the high-pressure to the low-pressure zone. This is especially true in large areas, such as this book store. In operating in narrow areas, such as hallways, the fog stream impinging on the walls and ceiling may create an adequate shield for the protection of the fire fighters.

4. This is a definite possibility. Where the heat is too intense for a direct attack on a cellar or basement fire and there are no exterior openings from which water can be effectively used to reduce heat intensity, then one of the practical alternatives is to open the floor above for the insertion of cellar pipes or distributors.

The fact that the floor is 8-inches of reinforced concrete with utility piping hung from the under side of the floor aggravates the problem but does not prevent its accomplishment.

Before resorting to this alternative, consider the following:
a. Can you adequately ventilate the first floor to maintain line positions?
b. If you have to withdraw your companies, what will be the effect of the openings in respect to fire spread?
c. Will the shelving prevent hitting the fire?

    d.  Are there other alternatives that could accomplish the task without that element of risk introduced by openings between floors?

B. Reasons:
  5.  Firemen are generally experienced in operating in frame and non-fireproof construction, where the areas are much smaller, ventilation facilities better, and extinguishment faster. In this situation, they are operating in the basement of a large-area building, the smoke is dense, the atmosphere highly heated and they must endure this situation for a long period of time. They are not usually oriented to these surroundings. If a fireman panics, judgment ceases to function, and he will instinctively try to save himself, but his actions will be irrational. That is why it is so important to set up proper safety procedures for this type of fire situation.

      In true fireproof construction, the compartmentation will contain the fire. There is time to develop and enforce safety procedures. With large areas, large fires, and fireproof construction, organization is more important than speed.

  6.  In this particular fire, the commander established the following procedures to ensure the safety of his men.
    a.  Teams of three men and an officer were used. All of the men in each team were taken from the same company so they worked with men they knew.
    b.  For each line, there were three designated teams:
        1.  One team on the line.
        2.  One team on standby.
        3.  One team for relief.
    c.  All men wore self-contained breathing apparatus.
    d.  Roof ropes were stretched from the street and tied to a post in the book store. There were two such guide lines, and they were four to five feet above the walking surface, since hose lines in some places were covered with water, and not visible.
    e.  Searchlight units positioned lights within the passageways. Although the smoke was dense, the lights did help and provided means of identification of the

passageway. If you saw the light, you knew you were in the right passageway.

f. When it becomes evident to the commander that some of his firemen were becoming confused and in jeopardy, he established his safety procedures not only in respect to the book store, but to govern the entire operation. The men were forced to work according to the plan and no individual efforts were permitted. He knew he would extinguish the fire; it was only a question of time. Therefore, he stressed safety rather than aggressiveness.

7. To give us some guidance in this matter, the following research projects on the subject are related:

a. In school fire tests conducted by the Los Angeles Fire Department in 1959 and reported in "Operation School Burning," published by the NFPA, the temperature of 150° F at the five-foot level was selected as that at which teachers and children could not be expected to enter a corridor from a relatively cool room.

b. In fire tests conducted by the National Research Council of Canada, reported in the NFPA Quarterly of April 1960, 300° F was taken as the maximum survivable breathing temperature. A temperature this high can be endured only for a short period and if moisture is present—not at all.

c. Dr. Claudy, as a result of his work with the District of Columbia Fire Department, suggested 120° to 130° F as the limit beyond which trained firemen should not be exposed without protective breathing equipment. Even self-contained masks and full clothing can not protect men for more than 10 minutes in dry air at 180° to 190° F and for five minutes at temperatures of 160° to 165° F in steamy atmospheres.

d. In this particular fire situation, relief was provided every five minutes, and the relief period was for 10 minutes. This plan worked out satisfactorily since there were no injuries or heat exhaustion cases. To effectuate this plan, however, four additional engine companies had to be special-called, and it took six companies to keep two lines in operation.

e. Where arrangements can be made, a physician can render invaluable assistance at a fire situation of this type. He can help the chief determine the maximum operating time for a man, how often he can be exposed, and when a company should be returned to quarters and a new unit called for relief.

8. Increase the reach of the stream. A multiversal nozzle with a 1¼-inch tip, operating at a pressure of about 100 psi, may give the range to completely cover the book store. However, the problem may be that the shelving is preventing water from contacting the fire. Nevertheless, this procedure should be tried at this time since it is easy to effectuate.

9. Lines can now be taken down the west stairway into the Ramskeller, and the cinder or concrete partition breached to allow for stream penetration into the book store. Openings can be made into these partitions easily. Therefore, make as many as necessary to complete extinguishment quickly. ·The firemen will be operating in relative comfort in this area, since the gases and heat are exhausting rapidly at the east stairway.

### CONCLUSION

If lines can not advance to the seat of the fire, the problem is either lack of ventilation or the wind is driving the convection currents toward the incoming firemen. This was the concept that finally governed the chief in his final tactical procedures. In this fire, wind was not a factor, so it became evident that ventilation facilities had to be improved. It was finally decided that the easiest method, although unusual, was to break the Thermopane wall enclosing the stairway. Once this was done, the fire problem diminished rapidly.

This fire also shows that the successful strategist is the thinking chief. Remember, you cannot think and yell at the same time. In management, they talk about planning, which consists essentially of getting all the available facts and then considering all the alternative courses of action. Weigh the advantages and disadvantages of each alternative and then make the decision. A fire chief is the manager of a fire, and the same principles of management prevail.

# *Chapter 10*

# *Concepts*

In this chapter, the objective is to develop concepts or principles which will guide officers in their extinguishment procedures. A number of fire situations will be presented, followed by a series of questions pertaining to each situation. It is important that the student develop his own answers to these questions before matching his solutions with the answers given. Remember that tactical procedures may vary as long as the applicable basic principle is not violated. The important part of this chapter does not lie in positioning lines, but rather in the explanation and development of the concepts.

## CASE 1 (Figure 1)

When the first engine company arrives, they note fire blowing out of two front windows on the second floor of a 2-story, unoccupied, commercial building. The fire is in the front portion of the building. The area of the building is 20 X 60 feet.

Figure 1. *Don't change direction in which flames are blowing. Since combustion products are venting to the exterior, interior line advancement is facilitated.*

*1. What action should the first engine company perform?*

*2. Explain the reason for the action.*

*3. Develop the concept or principle that guides the action.*

1. Action
   Stretch a line up the interior stairway and move forward to fire area. Use stream to drive heat and smoke out of building, thereby continuing the original venting direction of the fire. Do not originally use exterior master streams.

2. Reason
   Large fires give off great quantities of combustible gases. They are heated beyond their ignition temperatures, and then rapid flaming combustion may require only additional oxygen.

   This fire is burning vigorously and venting at the windows. There is an inflow of oxygen from the opposite direction. To use a deck pipe, ladder pipe or elevating platform stream from the front of the building will force these combustion gases rearward and into an area of free oxygen.

   Where feasible, do not use heavy streams to push fire toward new fuel and additional oxygen.

3. Concept
   Where the fire is blowing out windows or otherwise venting safely to the exterior, position lines in such a manner as to maintain the flow of flame and hot gases to the exterior of the building.

**CASE 2 (Figure 2)**

On the second floor of a three-story, non-fireproof, commercial building, heavy fire develops in an occupancy storing mops, brooms, and similar material. The fire is pushing out of the front windows, and smoke and heat have permeated the narrow hallway on the second floor because of loose-fitting doors. The engine company finds the position untenable on the second floor, and heat conditions preclude any interior operations on the third floor.

Heavy streams must be directed into second and third floors, front, and rear and sides where possible.

Figure 2. *When heat intensity is so severe that interior positions cannot be maintained, exterior streams are warranted.*

*1. Explain the reasons for the action.*

*2. Develop the concept or principle that guides the action.*

1. Reasons for Action

   Heat buildup on the third floor will become more intense; then the floor will light up. To make an attempt to save this floor, you must cool the area and wet the combustible stock. The ladder company will vent at the roof level in an endeavor to get the heated gases to pillar into the atmosphere. Sweep as much of the ceiling area on second and third floors as the angle of penetration permits. Keep heavy stream appliances moving horizontally and vertically to attain your objectives.

When the engine company can move up the stairwell to the second floor level, shut down exterior streams and change to offensive strategy. However, if the exterior streams fail to darken fire because of poor penetration or other factors and the fire gains in momentum, then give primary consideration to structural failure and pursue a defensive strategy.

2. Concept

    When fire is threatening to extend from floor to floor, and forces cannot gain foothold in building, direct master streams in to fire floor and floors above fire to confine fire until a more direct attack can be developed.

**Figure 3.** *When there is inflow of flame at exterior windows, the fire is venting in another direction. Check the rear, or any interior arteries to determine channel of fire spread.*

**CASE 3 (Figure 3)**

At night, a large body of bright flame can be seen from the street in the interior of the second floor of a five-story non-fireproof, commercial building. No fire or smoke is pushing out of any front windows, even though some of the windows have been broken by the heat; but fire has vented through an interior shaft. There are no people in the building.

*ACTION*

Use master streams to darken fire on second floor, to break windows on the upper floors, and to penetrate the third floor.

*QUESTIONS*

*1. Explain the reason for the action.*

*2. Develop a concept or principle that guides the action.*

1. Reasons for the action

   Since this fire is already vented to the outer air in a substantial manner, its intensity will increase greatly in a short period of time.

   The exterior stream, or streams, will push the fire, heat and smoke in the direction in which the fire is already channeled. This is a distinct advantage. Furthermore, this stream should be directed into all the third-floor windows, sweeping the ceiling to the maximum degree possible. The water will drench the combustible material, making its ignition more difficult. Some of the free water will, under most conditions in a non-fireproof construction, penetrate to the floor below and thereby slow down combustion in this area.

   If the windows are of plain glass, heavy streams are effective in breaking the glass, and this procedure permits rapid venting of upper floors of the building.

   There is no advantage in originally pursuing an interior attack at this fire. The exterior streams are not spreading the fire, and they may quickly knock down the fire. Furthermore, companies operating inside would have to move against convected currents. This would considerably slow their progress or make progress impossible. Therefore, the objective in this fire situation is to darken fire with exterior streams and then move to interior offensive strategy. If the exterior streams fail to darken the fire and the fire further develops and extends, the probability of structural failure will force the commander to change his strategy to defensive.

   The shaft venting of this fire has advantages and disadvantages. For example, it establishes the channel by which this fire will spread, but it also localizes horizontal spread of the fire. Unless the fire is controlled in the early stages, the second-floor fire will burn through the ceilings and floors and envelop the third floor. In addition, the steam developed when the cool water hits the fire, will flow with the other gases to the shaft and dissipate up the shaft. This will decrease effectiveness of streams and will mean that water must be brought into direct contact with fire to cool it.

2. Concept

Where there is a large body of fire on a floor and the flame is not vigorously pushing out of windows, beware!—for the fire is venting through a shaft, stairway or similar vertical artery.

## CASE 4 (Figure 4)

Fire is blowing out of four windows on the fifth floor of a modern 18-story building.

Figure 4. *Water is flowed down face of the building to form a shield against fire extending above by auto-exposure. Care is exercised not to direct streams into fire floor or floors above.*

The first action by the first arriving engine company is to set up a master stream appliance and direct the stream in such a manner that it will hit the building face above the fire and the water will curtain the exposed windows.

*QUESTIONS*

*1. Justify this action.*

*2. Develop a concept or principle that guides the action.*

*ANSWERS*

1. Justification of Action
   If you did not set up this water curtain, the fire could extend by auto-exposure to many floors above the fire floor. The

heavy stream is the means of controlling the extension possibilities in the quickest possible time. As soon as the engine company on the fifth floor is ready to move in and extinguish the fire, the heavy stream must be shut down. Water flowing down the facing of the building will impede ventilation at the fifth-floor level and hinder or prevent the advancement of the interior line.

2. Concept
When fire is threatening to extend by auto-exposure, direct a hand line or deck pipe stream above the windows involved in such a manner that the water will flow down the facing of the building.

## CASE 5 (Figure 5)

The engine men are endeavoring to move a line with a combination fog and solid stream nozzle through a 60-foot long hallway to the rooms of an apartment. Although they are wearing self-contained breathing apparatus, the heat barrier is so great that their progress has been stopped, and they are now lying on the hallway floor, unable to come to grips with the fire.

*QUESTIONS*

*1. At fires of first-alarm proportions, when a line cannot advance to the seat of the fire, what is generally the cause?*

**Figure 5.** *Firemen cannot accomplish the impossible. The heat barrier is too intense. Commanding officers must be aware of and implement feasible alternatives.*

*2. Develop the concept or principle that guides the action.*

*ANSWERS*

1. Explanation

When fire attains a vigorous level of combustion, temperatures elevate rapidly. Temperatures of 1200° F at the ceiling level and 300° F at the 5-foot level are not uncommon. These temperatures are fatal to humans. Therefore, as the line advances, the water must cool the atmosphere and the convection currents must flow away from the advancing firemen. If the line is moving from the front, there must be adequate openings in the rear to exhaust the convection heat.

If you have adequate ventilation and the line cannot proceed down the hallway, check on the wind direction. If the wind velocity is high and blowing the convection currents in the direction of the firemen, advancement of line ceases. Then, for effectiveness, tactics must change and the firemen must move into the area from the opposite direction with the wind at their backs.

2. Concept

Where lines cannot move because of a heat barrier, increase venting facilities. If that does not work, consider movement from other directions.

*Note:* This concept was used in guiding the actions of the chief at a fire in a college building (Chapter 9) and will act as a guide in development of the action in the next case.

## CASE 6 (Figure 6)

A large body of fire is raging in the northeast portion of a 100 X 200-foot, one-story, non-fireproof grocery warehouse. There are entrances to the warehouse on three different streets. The wind is very mild. The heat intensity is preventing a close approach to the fire. Three engine companies respond to the fire.

Figure 6. *Utilize streams to localize fire until roof ventilation can be accomplished.*

*1. Position the engine companies.*

*2. Give an explanation.*

*3. Develop the conept or principle that guides the action.*

1. Action
   Position companies at the three openings that exist at the street floor level. Their purpose is to reduce heat and confine the fire to as small an area as possible until the ladder company can effect ventilation, especially at the roof level.

2. Explanation
   Since the wind is mild in this situation, the commander should concentrate on increasing ventilation.

   Heat is a substantial barrier. It can stop the advancement of a company even though its personnel are equipped with self-contained breathing units and fog nozzles. Once the roof is adequately vented, the hot gases will quickly seek the roof openings. The hot gases, because of their expansion, will flow rapidly out the roof opening and there will be a proportional inflow of cool air through the many door and window openings. This condition permits the engine companies to move rapidly toward the fire area.

3. Concept
   Where the fire is in a large-area building and the heat intensity prevents a close approach, use a pincer movement to defend against further spread until ventilation permits a more direct attack.

## CASE 7 (Figure 7)

Fire originates in a paper baling occupancy in a one-story, brick building, 40 X 150 feet. The roof is of unpierced concrete construction, and all window openings are closed with 4-inches of brick. There are two large doors in the building, one in the front and one at a side about 40-feet from the front.

*ACTION AND EXPLANATION*

Three engine companies with 1½-inch hose equipped with fog nozzles entered from the side door. As the streams were directed toward the front of building, the steam, smoke and heat were ventilated through the front door. But as the streams were directed toward the west and south walls, the steam, smoke and heat bounced against the walls and enveloped the fire fighters. Visibility was reduced to zero.

The chief ordered the companies to use their water intermittently and only enough to maintain their interior positions.

Figure 7. *Complete extinguishment was postponed until adequate ventilation was provided.*

*1. Justify the order of the chief.*

*2. Develop the concept or principle that guides the action.*

*ANSWERS*

1. The chief's objective was to maintain an interior position while the ladder companies were removing the bricks from the window openings and using pneumatic drills to pierce the concrete roof. When the water from a hose line makes contact with a burning area, a great deal of steam is generated and the burning substance, depending upon its nature, can then emit great quantities of smoke. When you hit a bale of paper with a hose stream, the flame may disappear, but the smoke emitted from the bale increases. The chief is trying to keep the generation of smoke within the vent capacities of available openings.

It is equally important to maintain a proper thermal balance within the interior of the building, whereby the smoke will flow from the interior of the building to the exterior. To accomplish this, maintain a higher temperature inside the building than outside. The greater the disparity between the hotter inside and cooler outside temperatures, the greater will be the velocity of smoke flow toward the outside. Hit the fire when necessary, but try at this time to avoid sweeping the ceiling with the streams. Over-application of water results in a cold smoke, which is stagnant and physiologically damaging to firefighters.

2. Concept

Do not generate more smoke and steam than can be adequately ventilated. Or, use streams only in proportion to your vent facilities.

Maintain a thermal balance whereby the interior temperature is considerably higher, especially at the ceiling level, than the outside temperature.

**CASE 8 (Figure 8)**

A fire originates in rubbish in the vicinity of a dumbwaiter shaft at the cellar level in a non-fireproof apartment house. The shaft door is open in the cellar, and on the arrival of the first engine company, heavy fire is pushing up the dumbwaiter shaft. Presume that there is no life hazard.

Three engines respond to this fire.

*QUESTIONS*

*1. Where would you position the three lines?*

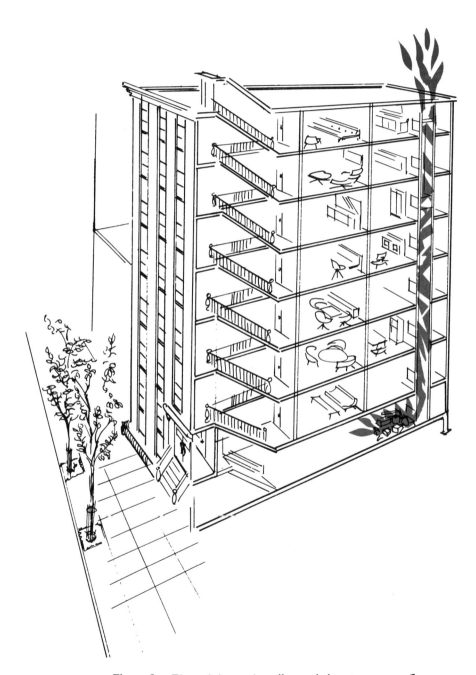

Figure 8. *Fire originates in cellar and threatens upper floors.*

*2. Give an explanation.*

*3. Develop the concept or principle that guides the action.*

1. Action
    A. Stretch first line up the interior stairway to the highest floor level that can be reached while awaiting water in the line—usually the third floor. Take line to door of dumb-waiter shaft, direct stream upwards in the shaft to darken down fire, then shut down and take line to top floor to cover possible extension there.
    B. The second line is stretched to cellar to check horizontal spread and to extinguish fire.

C. The third line is stretched up interior stairs to back up first line and extinguish any fire which may spread to the various floors.

2. Explanation

If the dumbwaiter doors are in the closed position, the fire will not originally spread to the apartments bordering on the shaft, but invariably, there are spaces around pipes, electrical conduits or wires, which permit fire to travel into ceiling spaces and to a greater degree into the cockloft. Since the cockloft is heavily fireloaded and since the life hazard usually is greatest at the top floor, the objective of the first line is to douse the flames in the shaft, get to the top floor, and control fire in this area and in the hanging ceiling.

The officer calls for water in line as soon as the hose stretch is started. With a quick hook-up to the pumper, the water will be delivered to hose line at about the time the firemen reach the third floor. From this position, the range of the stream will readily reach the top of the shaft.

If the vertical extension can be controlled, this fire remains a first-alarm operation. If the fire in the shaft continues to develop, there will be major extension of fire to some of the apartments bordering the shaft, and the volume of fire will be beyond first-alarm stages. The objective is first to keep the fire to one floor level and then to as small an area on that floor as possible. Therefore, the second line is stretched to the cellar area, to cut off the horizontal extension.

In stairway and shaft fires, whether they be vent or dumbwaiter shafts, the first line should be backed up with a second line to ensure the safety of the personnel on the first line and to accelerate extinguishment of the fire. Therefore, the third engine company is ordered to stretch up the stairway to reinforce the first engine company.

3. Concept

When a fire threatens serious extension vertically, the first line should be deployed when possible, to control the vertical extension. When vertical extension has been checked, give consideration to horizontal spread of fire.

**CASE 9 (Figure 9)**

At 2 a.m. a heavy body of fire erupted through the roof of a super market exposing two apartment houses, each of which is five-stories high, 25 X 60 feet in area, and with many window openings facing the supermarket. The wind is brisk and from the west.

Figure 9. *Serious supermarket fire exposes two tenement buildings.*

*1. Where should the first master stream be positioned?*

*2. Where should the first hand line be positioned?*

*3. At what point in the operation would an engine company be assigned to Building A?*

*4. Explain the reasons that guide the assignments.*

*5. Develop the concept or principle that guides the action.*

1. Position the first master stream to protect the west wall of Building B, allowing its water to flow over the windows, shielding them insofar as possible from the flame and heat of the mass of fire.

2. Hand lines should be stretched into Building B to cover stairways, shafts and to extinguish fire within rooms.

3. Building B must first be protected; only then can companies be assigned to Building A.

4. Explanation

Buildings on the leeward are exposed by radiation and convection, while buildings on the windward are exposed primarily by radiation. When the wind is blowing convection columns into the exposed building, the danger is critical, and unless immediate and concentrated action is taken, the fire will burn toward the shafts and stairways, trapping many people. In Building A on the other hand, the fire spread will be comparatively slow. The wind draft is in the direction of Building B, and although there may be some extension of fire to curtains, drapes, etc. in Building A, later arriving companies will have no serious difficulty in controlling this situation.

5. Concept

Provide earlier and heavier exposure protection for buildings to the leeward side than buildings to the windward side of a fire.

**CASE 10 (Figure 10)**

A series of covered piers along the waterfront are joined to a two-story bulkhead structure built along the marginal street. Pier B is well involved in fire and the wind is blowing the fire toward Pier C and along the bulk-head structure in the direction of C. All the companies have been assigned to protect against this extension of fire. On your arrival, the wind direction changes, and now Pier A is in jeopardy.

*ACTION*

1. Insofar as possible, call additional companies to cope with new fire front.
2. Maintain present defensive line.

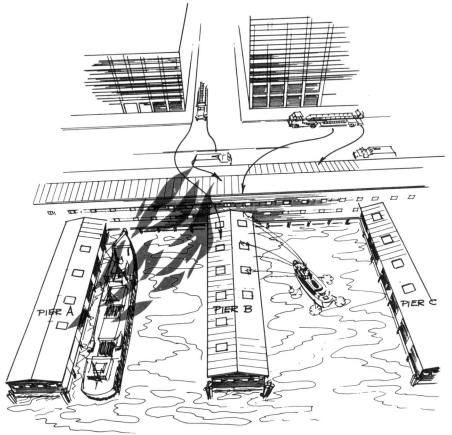

**Figure** 10. *It is difficult to reposition units already in operation at major alarms. It is generally preferable to use standby and additional units to cope with new fire developments caused by a changing wind.*

*QUESTIONS*

*1. Explain the reasons for the action.*

*2. Develop the concept or principle that guides the action.*

1. Reasons for Action

   If wind changes direction, it can change direction again. If the defending companies are reassigned to protect Pier A and the bulkhead structure running in the direction of Pier A, the defensive line protecting Pier C now becomes vulnerable if the variable wind again changes. Furthermore, repositioning companies may take as long a period of time as awaiting the arrival of new companies. A few of the portable lines may readily be repositioned, but for the most part, it is better to retain your positioned forces and use standby and later arriving companies to cope with the new developments.

2. Concept

   At very large fires, once a defensive line has been established, endeavor to retain it and do not move your positioned forces to cope with extensions in other directions.

## CASE 11 (Figure 11)

In a railroad freight yard, several trains of freight cars are laid up on adjacent tracks. The freight cars are loaded with a variety of hazardous materials, and some have unidentified cargoes. On a nearby loading platform, several dozen cylinders of a compressed flammable gas are stored. A partially loaded trailer truck is parked at one end of the loading platform.

Upon arrival, heavy fire is found in the railroad freight office, which is part of the same structure housing the warehouse and loading platform. Fire is extending rapidly under influences of a brisk wind, and considerable sparks are being thrown off, falling over the entire yard.

The freight yard is on the outskirts of the city. Response is slow, for apparatus must move with extreme care within the freight yard, and hydrants are remote.

*ACTION*

The hazardous contents of the various freight cars and tank cars would create an extremely dangerous condition if involved. Due to the difficulty of stretching lines, considerable thought and effort must be given to removing as many freight cars, tank cars, trailer trucks, and cylinders of compressed gases as can be done in the time available.

Figure 11. *A railroad freight office fire exposes movable cylinders of compressed gas, a truck and railroad rolling stock.*

Lines must be positioned to cover the exposure of these dangerous materials, and must be located between the fire and the serious exposures.

*QUESTION*

*Develop the concept that guides the action.*

*ANSWER*

Concept
When a fire creates severe exposure problems and either the fire or the fuel, or a major portion thereof, can be moved to a safer location, make every effort to do so in the initial fire operations.

**CASE 12 (Figure 12)**

Fire started in Building B and has extended by radiation to Building A. Fire also has extended by convection and radiation in major proportions to the exterior and interior of Building C. To the leeward are several similar structures not yet involved but imminently threatened. Smoke wisps are arising from them. Each of the structures shown is a three-story and attic, frame rooming house. Since it is winter, these beach rooming houses are unoccupied and closed. The distance between the frame buildings is 25-feet. Further to the leeward are several blocks of similar type structures.

Two engine companies respond to this situation.

Figure 12. *A fire in a frame rooming house threatens similar buildings in a beach resort area; apparatus response is limited to two engine companies.*

*1. State the action.*

*2. Give reasons for the action.*

*3. Develop the concept that guides the action.*

1. The two engine companies will concentrate on setting up master streams to protect Buildings D and E. Because of the spacing of the buildings, some of the master streams can be used not only to keep Building D wet, but used intermittently to darken some of the exterior fire in Building C. Hand lines should be stretched to protect the interior of Buildings D and E, especially D.

2. Reasons
   If the original companies were assigned to Building A, B and C, the fire would surely extend to Buildings D and E and to other buildings on other streets to the leeward. The original companies must first attempt to cut off extension to the leeward before coping with the original fire buildings. Otherwise, the companies will be chasing fire from one street to another.

3. Concept
   Don't chase fire; get ahead of it.

**CASE 13 (Figure 13)**

Fire originated in the stairwell on the first story of a four-story residential building. It has extended up the stairwell and is jeopardizing the apartments on the second, third and fourth floors.

*QUESTIONS*

*1. Discuss the condition of the stairwell at the time of arrival of the first engine company.*

2. *What orders should the chief issue to the officers in charge of Engines 1 and 2?*

3. *Should the first engine company, in their endeavor to reach the top floors, pass fire?*

4. *Explain the procedures for advancing a hose line from the first to the top floor.*

*5. Develop the concept or principle that guides the action.*

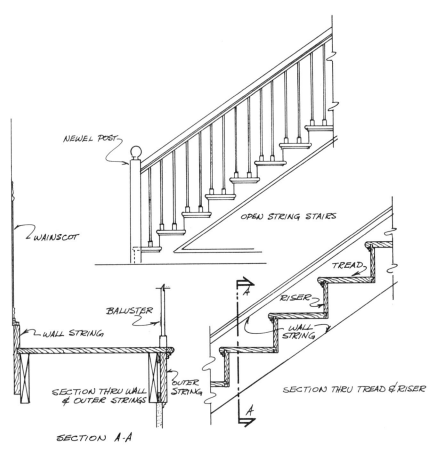

**Figure 13.**   *The fire loading of a non-combustible stairway is severe. When combined with the updraft of air, the stairway fire accelerates in intensity and spreads with frightening speed.*

1. When the fire is traveling up interior stairs, invariably the structural members of the stairs, such as the stair stringer, balustrade, newel post, tread and risers are made of wood. Although the partition separating the stairwell from the apartments will generally be of incombustible material, wood wainscoting and wood doors leading to the apartments are common. The fire loading, consequently, is severe, and when bulkhead scuttle or skylight above the stairs is opened, there will be a substantial draught of fresh air rising in the stairwell. These conditions will generate an intense fire.

2. If there is structural failure of the stairwell, this will complicate and impede fire operations. The chief, therefore, should make every effort to preserve the structural stability of the stairway. The first and second engine companies should be assigned to stretch lines to the interior stairway.

3. There is a saying in fire circles, "Do not pass fire, otherwise the fire fighters may be trapped." This is a good maxim, but like other words of wisdom, may be taken too literally. The engine company advancing up the stairway will knock down the major flame, but certainly will not try to cope with smoldering fire, such as in a mattress or a closet. As soon as the chief can get a second hose line into the stairway, the men on the first hose line can become more daring and expeditiously move forward to their objective—the top floor of the building.

4. When advancing a line up the stairs, the stream should first be directed upwards, preferably through the well hole, to cool the excessive heat and wet the burning material. A 2¹/₂-inch line with a combination fog and solid stream tip can accomplish this most effectively. It provides the mass of water necessary for cooling and the reach necessary to penetrate to the upper floors. It will require more effort on the part of the firemen than a 1¹/₂-inch line, but the additional amount of water and reach may be the factors that will help preserve the structural stability of the stairs.

The fire in the first flight of stairs should then be extinguished, the stream shut down, and a line advanced up to the second flight. Room fires should then be darkened, and, if the tenants have already been removed, the doors to the stairway should be temporarily closed. Direct the stream upward to cool the third floor, and then complete the extinguishment of the fire in the second flight. Again shut down the stream and advance to the third floor.

The reason for shutting down the stream when advancing the line is to make the task of getting the line to the top floor less difficult and to get it there with the greatest alacrity. It is almost impossible for an ordinary company of five men to advance a line of $2^1/_2$-inch hose up a stairway when the stream is in operation. Consider the weight of the hose, the water in the hose, the force of the nozzle reaction and the fact that men climbing the stairs must lift their own weight with one leg, and the impracticality of the feat becomes obvious.

If the flight of stairs to the fourth floor has been burned away, a line of hose should be sent up an aerial ladder or fire escape to the top floor. This line will darken the fire on the top floor. When the ceilings have been pulled, the water is to be directed into the cockloft space.

5. *Concept*
Give primary consideration to maintaining the structural stability of the principal means of access to the floors of the building.

## CASE 14 (Figure 14)

Three engine companies are positioned on the leeward front of a large area lumber yard fire. Their deck pipe streams are operating at maximum volume and reach. Nevertheless, the fire continues to develop in the piles beyond the reach of the master streams. The heat is growing more intense and the company officers are contemplating withdrawal. At this time, the chief arrives with additional engine companies. The wind is blowing toward the shed with a velocity of 15 mph.

Figure 14. *Protect personnel and apparatus holding the leeward position.*

## QUESTIONS

1. *If the three engine companies withdraw from their leeward positions, the Acme Lumber Company shed is doomed. What action may save the shed?*

*2. Develop the concept or principle that guidesthe action.*

1. With a wind velocity of 15 mph, the convection currents will very likely flow above the roof of the lumber shed. It is the radiant heat that is causing the difficulties. To try to set up a water curtain between the firemen and the fire would be ineffective. The best and fastest protection would be to engulf the apparatus and the men in fog streams. Therefore, the incoming engine companies would be used for this purpose. They could shield themselves from some radiant heat rays by operating master stream appliances from Leonard St., directing them upwardly and letting the water flow in such a manner that an umbrella of water will protect the men and apparatus. If the exposed engine company personnel can, in this manner, maintain their positions, this will provide time for the chief to get additional master or super streams in operation.

   The engine companies operating on Ralph St., to further protect the Acme Lumber Shed, will have to direct water on the facade of the Acme Lumber Shed facing the lumber yard.

2. *Concept*

   In large fire situations, try, insofar as possible, to maintain your leeward position. Use heat shields or fog streams to protect fire fighters from intolerable heat conditions.

**CASE 15 (Figure 15)**

Fire orginates in a grocery and meat market on the first floor of a three-story frame tenement. It is nighttime and the life hazard is severe. Other similar buildings adjoin the fire building on both sides. The fire has vented through an interior light and air shaft, immediately threatening major fire extension to upper floors of the fire building and exposure 4.

The first engine company stretches a line to the second floor of the fire building, to get a line between the fire and the occupants.

The second engine company performs in the same fashion in the exposure 4.

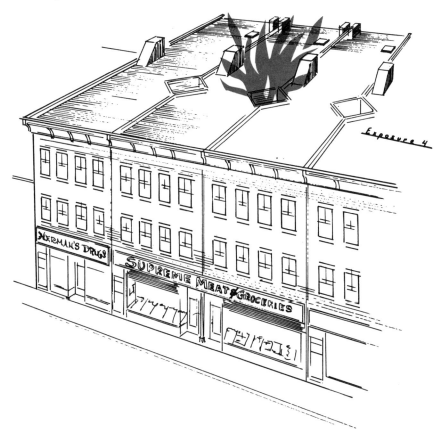

Figure 15. *For inside fire fighting, it is usually best to first attack source of fire rather than its extensions.*

*QUESTIONS*

*1. Comment on the action.*

*2. State the concept or principle that guides the proper action in this situation.*

*ANSWERS*

1. The engine company operating above the fire will be severely limited in advancing its hose line through the hallway and rooms to the shaft, since the heat and smoke of the store fire will rise through the shaft and floor boards and attain intolerable proportions. Unless the major fire in the store is hit directly and the source of the heat checked to a degree, search, rescues, and confinement of the fire will be greatly impeded by the heat and smoke conditions. Since the original fire continues to burn without the cooling affects of water, it will become larger and larger and the confinement lines operating above will be driven to the stairwell

The line in Exposure 4 will be more successful since the operating crew is not sitting on an inferno of fire.

The first hose lines should be stretched into the store to quickly cool the major part of the fire. This action will greatly enhance the chances of searching and evacuating the building and confining the fire. The chief could position five engine companies above the fire, but they would be ineffective unless the main body of fire on the first floor is cooled.

In the supermarket fire in Chapter 2, there was no choice, for if the companies entered the basement level from the rear, the impact of their streams would have pushed the fire up the open stairways.

2. *Concept*

It is usually best, in interior operations, to hit the source of fire, then head it off.

*Chapter 11*

# Panic and Use of Fog
# Streams for Ventilation Purposes

**PANIC**

Superheated gases that flow to upper floors of a building by means of stairways, elevator shafts, air-conditioning systems and voids within the structure account for the greatest death toll in many fire situations. When people are trapped in the unfamiliar atmosphere of superheated gases, it is only natural for them to temporarily lose their sense of judgment. The fire chief, in these situations, will be dealing with an irrational group of people. Therefore, the fire strategist should endeavor to develop a background or understanding of panic conditions, so that he is better able to command in these fire situations.

236

## FOG STREAMS FOR VENTILATION PURPOSES

The fire forces have always had to contend with the rise of convection gases in structures and their deadly effect on people above the fire floor. But generally, fire fighters could alleviate or diminish smoke permeation within a fire building by roof and window ventilation. However, with the growth of high rise structures throughout many communities, there has arisen a situation caused by the deficiencies in these structures, whereby, within a matter of seconds or minutes, deadly gases can entomb people in stairways, elevators and the upper floors of these buildings. How can we change the atmosphere in these tall structures from deadly to normal so that many lives can be spared? The only equipment available to cope with these situations is fans and fog. streams. The law governing the motion of gases and the mechanics of moving gases must now become an indispensable part of the fire fighters' knowledge. The fire officer of tomorrow will have to become as knowledgeable in the field of aerodynamics as today's fire officer is in the field of hydraulics. This chapter touches on only a few of the related points. In a later volume on fighting fires in high-rise structures, the subject will be given further scope.

## FIRE SITUATION—PUBLIC ASSEMBLY HALL

Fire originates at 9 p.m. in the basement of on old, 40 × 100-foot, two-story structure, and travels up the unenclosed, combustible stairway to the second floor, and vents through the open bulkhead door at the roof. The stores on the first floor are closed for the evening, but on the second floor, there is a large public assembly hall in which a well attended political rally is being held.

The chief, on arrival, notes that he has near-panic conditions among the people on the second floor. The fire has vented itself, and no flame has entered the second floor, but the smoke condition is extremely severe because in addition to a good body of fire, there are also 10 bins of sawdust burning and smoldering in the basement. The entire building and the area are enveloped in a pungent smoke. (Figure 1)

Figure 1.   *Fire has cut off the primary egress for 2nd floor occupants. Smoke is acrid and has penetrated all areas of the building. Panic prevails.*

There is a fire escape on the front of the building, but it is being overtaxed by the many people trying to simultaneously exit from the second floor.

There is a 4 × 10-foot fireproof corridor leading from a rear building to the basement of the fire building.

**A. Panic**

    1. When we say that a person panics, just what changes take place in this person?

    2. What is the cause of panic?

    3. Do all people react to disasters in about the same manner?

4. Why is it extremely dangerous to have a few people panic within a large group?

5. In theater fires, the risk of being crushed to death has not deterred some in the audience from stampeding a single exit, even though other exits were obviously available. How can such unreasonable acts be performed by rational beings?

6. In the above example, what would be the outstanding characteristic of panic?

7. Since the person in panic loses the power of reasoning, will he nevertheless attempt to save himself?

8. When confronted with a situation where panic exists, what should be the primary thought of the fire commander?

9. Can a person in panic be jolted out of his confusion by slapping him in the face, dousing him with cold water or other forms of abuse?

10  How can reason be restored?

11. What steps should the chief take to cope with the panic conditions?

## B. Fog Fan

1. The natural ventilation was inadequate in this situation. The dense fumes from sawdust continued to mushroom throughout the structure even though the roof door and many windows on the second floor were open. The chief ordered two $2^{1}/_{2}$-inch fog lines to the first floor level. One of the streams was directed upward and darkened the massive fire in the stairwell. The other stream was directed down the stairway toward the basement to cut off upward extension of fire. After the first stream had darkened the fire in the stairwell, then both streams were directed down the stairwell from the first floor. There were windows in the front of the basement and a basement door leading to a corridor in the rear of the building. The windows and the door were opened. Will

these fog lines assist the ventilating of the stairwell and the second floor assembly hall? Discuss this procedure.

2. Firemen stretched a line from the adjoining street, entered the corridor and opened the 2½-inch fog nozzle about 10 feet back from the basement entrance. What effect would this have on air movement in the basement? Discuss in respect to front windows opened and closed.

3. How should the nozzle be operated while in the corridor?

4.  At this time the panic was under control, and the two lines, operating at the top of the basement stairs were no longer directed into the basement to induce ventilation. Instead, the lines set up a stream barrier to prevent fire from rising in the stairwell. This made it easier for the engine company in the corridor to expeditiously move a 2½-inch line from the rear to the front of the basement and extinguish the surface flame. Although the fire was under control, the smoke-laden basement continued to be troublesome.

    The chief had the option of augmenting ventilation with a 5000–cfm fan or a 2½-inch fog stream. Which is more effective?

5.  In order to eject the greatest amount of smoke from the front basement windows, what is the best nozzle position?

6. The basement area is 40 × 100 feet with 10-foot ceilings. Using a 2½-inch fog stream, with a flow of 250 gpm, how long will it take to completely change the atmosphere within the basement, presuming there are adequate intake and discharge ports?

*ANSWERS*

**A. Panic**
1. a. His judgement ceases to function.
   b. He is motivated primarily by an overwhelming and infectious fear.
2. A sudden change of environment to which an intellectual adjustment has not been made.
3. a. No.
   b. Certain emotional types will panic immediately.
   c. A stable individual may react calmly to the disaster.
   d. However, the stable individual may be so over-whelmed by later events that he, too, panics.
4. Because a very small number of individuals in true panic can easily precipitate headlong mass flight of a crowd.
5. a. They have temporarily lost their capacity to reason.
   b. Therefore, at this moment they are not rational beings, but animals.
6. Its blindness.
   a. Lack of all judgment.
   b. Animality of man.
   c. Unreasoning fear.
   d. Contagiousness.

7. a. Yes.
   b. He will instinctively try to save himself but without the guidance of judgment.
   c. Therefore, at a fire he may jump from a high floor to escape the highly heated gases of combustion. His fear of the gases is so overpowering, he will not consider the dangers of jumping.
8. He should try to restore the reasoning of people on the verge of panic.
9. a. The psychiatrists say no.
   b. Such tactics may interrupt the disorganized behavior at least briefly.
   c. But in the midst of disaster tensions, striking a disturbed person will not only fail as a rule to control his panic, but will greatly increase the anxiety of those around him who may feel on the verge of panic themselves.
10. a. Those persons in complete panic perhaps can not be helped other than by directly saving them.
    b. The person on the verge of panic can have his reason restored by taking authoritative command of the situation, providing him with the means by which he can save himself and setting a good example under the trying circumstances.
11. a. Try to restore confidence of the people. This can be done to some extent by positioning some firemen in full fire-fighting gear at the second floor level. People will see the firemen confidently walking among them, offering assistance and direction.
    b. Eliminate the cause of the panic. This can be accomplished by getting lines to extinguish the fire in the stairway, and to cut off fire at top of the basement stairs. This will be the assignments for Engines 1 and 2. Ladder personnel will completely ventilate building.
    c. The third category of activity consists of removing the people from the dangerous area. This will consist essentially of raising ladders to second floor windows and fire escapes and removing people via interior stairs when it is safe to do so.

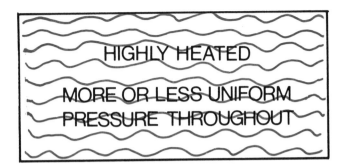

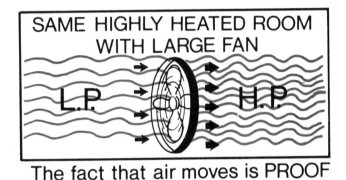

Figure 2. *Comparison of fire-created atmospheric conditions.*

## IMMEDIATELY BEHIND NOZZLE

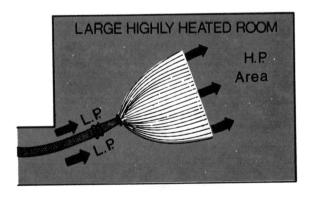

Figure 3. *High and low pressure differential created by fog stream.*

**B. Fog Fan (Figures 2 and 3)**

1. Yes. Fog streams operated to give a flow of 250 gpm will induce an air flow of 8798 cfm. Therefore, the chief by using two 2½-inch fog streams will cause a massive air flow from the second floor and stairway toward the basement area.

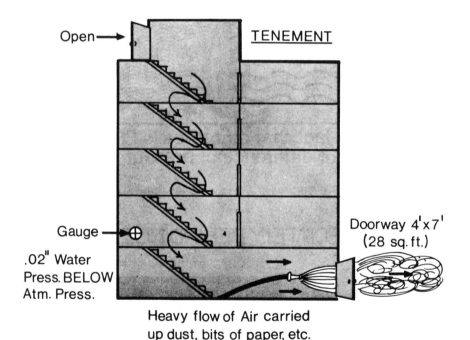

Heavy flow of Air carried
up dust, bits of paper, etc.

When nozzle reversed and directed
into building, pressure on 2nd floor
was .02 water ABOVE Atm. Pressure

Figure 4.

A fog stream acts as a fan. In front of the fan it will create a high pressure zone and behind the nozzle, a low pressure zone. In an experiment conducted in New York City, a fog nozzle was placed in a hall at the front of the stairs in a vacant tenement building and directed at the door to the street. All doors to the apartments in the

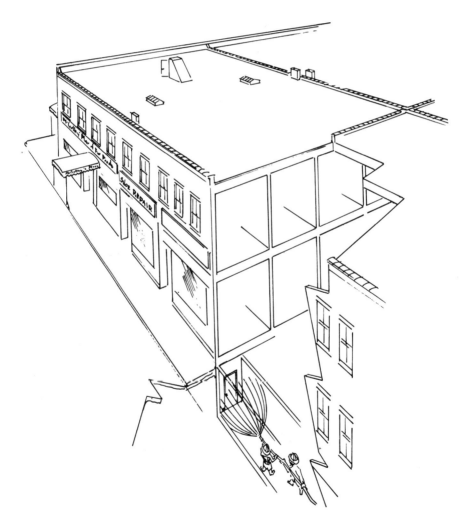

Figure 5. *Firemen are advancing a fog stream down a fireproof corridor toward the fire area.*

building were closed. The bulkhead door at the roof was open. Thus, the halls and stairways formed a closed direct system through which any air movement could be noted. When the fog nozzle was operated at 100 psi, a heavy flow of air poured down through the halls and stairways of the building. Pieces of paper were sucked directly down the stairs without falling to the floor, and they disappeared in the fog cone. (Figure 4)

# DANGERS OF MISAPPLICATION

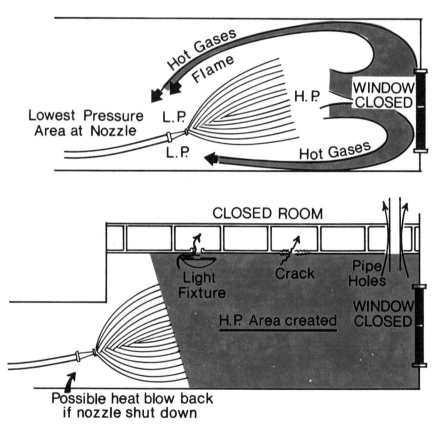

Figure 6. *Adequate ventilation must take place ahead of fog streams, otherwise men can be seriously burned.*

Of course, in this fire situation, the door on the second floor is opened and so are the windows on this floor. This will diminish the effectiveness of the flow of smoke toward the basement, but since a negative pressure will be created in the stairwells, the smoke will move from the second floor toward the basement.

2. If the combined open window area at the front of the basement is equal to the area of the corridor, and the corridor is served by adequate open suction channels from the adjoining street, a heavy flow of air will occur through the corridor, all of which will be discharged through the open basement windows. (Figure 5)

# Widest Pattern

# Adjusted to Just Miss Touching Wall

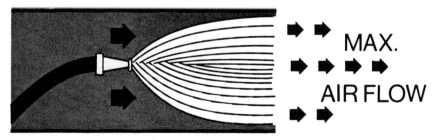

Figure 7.  *In moving a fog stream down a hallway, endeavor to adjust the fog so that it barely impinges on the corridor walls and ceiling.*

If no discharge ports are provided and this technique is employed, no flow will occur through the corridor, but the air and gas in the fire room will be placed under some compression. When the nozzle is shut down, the gas will discharge back into the hall. During the time that the fire room is under a relatively high pressure, the heated air and gas will flow into any and all breaks in the walls and ceilings which connect with an area of lower pressure. Final discharge ports should be as large as possible. (Figure 6)

3. The fog stream should be adjusted so that it just falls short of striking the walls and ceilings. In this manner maximum air velocity is obtained. The flow of air will be retarded if the fog cone is expanded to its widest pattern. (Figure 7)

4. Two senior instructors, Charles J. Wright and William J. Phaehler, at the University of Maryland, with technical assistance from the Mechanical Engineering Department conducted a series of tests with fans and fog streams and reported in Fire Engineering in March, 1971 that the greater effectiveness of fog streams as compared with smoke ejectors or fans is apparent. Fog streams are up to four times as effective.

5. In the University of Maryland experiment, tests showed that the best nozzle position is a few feet inside the room but near enough to the openings so that a fog pattern of about 55 to 60 degrees covers about 85-90 percent of the opening. The findings were:

*Table 1. Placement of Fog Streams*

| Position | Air Veloc., Ft. per Sec. | CFM of Air Moved |
|---|---|---|
| About 2 ft. outside side window | 370 | 1961 |
| At window opening | 680 | 3604 |
| Inside window, 55 to 60 degrees for pattern covering 85 to 90% of the opening | 1020 | 5406 |

(Nozzle flowing 60 gpm at 100 psi on a 1½-inch line.)

Figure 8. *The efficient use of a fog stream for ventilation on the left is compared with the inefficient use on the right.*

6. The 40 X 100 X 10 dimensions equal 40,000 cubic feet. A 2½-inch fog line with a flow of 250 gpm creates a discharge of approximately 8000 cubic feet of air per minute. Therefore, it will take approximately five minutes. The following table is the result of the tests at the University of Maryland mentioned in answers 4 and 5.

| Size Hose Line | * GPM Flow | Air Velocity Feet per Second | Cubic Feet per Minute of Air Moved |
|---|---|---|---|
| 1½ inch | 60 | 1,020 | 5,406 |
| 1½ inch | 95 | 1,270 | 6,731 |
| 1½ inch | 125 | 1,260 | 6,678 |
| 2½ inch | 125 | 1,340 | 7,102 |
| 2½ inch | 175 | 1,400 | 7,420 |
| 2½ inch | 250 | 1,660 | 8,798 |

Note the discrepancy with the 125-gpm nozzle, 1½-inch hose. Apparently, nozzles of different design produce varying exit velocities from the tip, so performance will vary even among nozzles of the same gallonage but produced by different manufacturers.

*Note:* The smoke-laden atmosphere is completely displaced within the five-minute period, but since the bales of sawdust will continue to smolder, ventilation must continue until fire is completely extinguished.

*Chapter 12*

# *Fires in Frame Buildings*

As far as fighting fires is concerned, there is little difference between wood frame residential buildings and those with brick exterior walls and internal wood structural material. The major advantage of a brick exterior wall is its ability to greatly limit the chances of fire spreading to an adjacent building. If the exterior walls become involved, a wood frame building will burn with greater intensity, of course, and expose nearby structures more readily than a brick-joist structure. Otherwise, fire will spread inside either type building in much the same manner.

## DETACHED ONE AND TWO-FAMILY RESIDENCES

In balloon construction of wood frame homes, the vertical spaces between the studs extend from the foundation to the attic, while in platform construction, some degree of fire-stopping is provided at each floor by the subflooring and the sole. But even in platform construction type, the channels for fire to spread vertically and horizontally are so numerous that a fire of any real intensity can quickly reach the attic or cockloft.

The older type of residence with lath and plaster walls, substantial doors and generally better workmanship offers somewhat better construction than newer residences, which often have hollow doors, wallboard, open archways, combustible ceiling tile and thin paneling.

### SMOLDERING FIRES

A small fire in upholstered furniture in a living room can generate enough toxic gases to reach bedrooms and put the occupants in a dazed or unconscious condition in a short time. A spray from a small diameter hose can quickly extinguish the fire, but fire fighters must always be alert to the carbon monoxide danger. This means that they must immediately ventilate all sections of the building and make a thorough search for incapacitated occupants.

### BASEMENT OR CELLAR FIRES

A line must immediately be taken to the interior stairs to fight a basement, or cellar, fire. When the heat prevents men from descending the stairs, the line should be held there to prevent the fire from extending upward and another line should be taken to the outside cellar entrance. If there is no outside cellar entrance, a fog stream should be directed through one of the windows to the flaming section of the cellar. If the fog stream does what it is expected to do, the generation of steam in great volume will make it necessary for the inside hose crew to keep the cellar door closed until steam generation subsides with the drop in temperature in the cellar. The alternative is to open a cellar window beyond the fire to permit the escape of steam and fire gases during the attack with the line at the first cellar window.

Ladder company members must quickly check all floors above the cellar, including the attic or cockloft, for indications of fire spread. Where partitions are hot and paint is blistering, or smoke is pushing out around baseboards, openings must be quickly made to introduce water and contain the fire.

Attic fires cause considerable difficulty because of the intense buildup of heat in the usually narrow stairway—or perhaps a hatchway—to the attic. Dormer and gable windows should be opened from the outside as soon as a fog nozzle has begun to operate. In large attics, it may be necessary to use a fog nozzle through a window to reduce the heat enough for a hand line to advance up the inside stairs or hatchway. Other alternatives are cellar pipes or distributors inserted through the roof.

### *FIRE THREATENING UPSTAIRS BEDROOMS*

When fire on the first floor is moving toward second floor bedrooms, a line must be quickly moved into the first floor to extinguish surface flame and then must be advanced aggressively up the stairs in an effort to cool down the fire before it enters the bedrooms. There can be no procrastination in the movement of this line. The heat will be intense, and there is always the tendency to cool the fire from the door entrance. But only limited fire can be hit from this position. Any delay in line movement may result in death for some of the occupants.

While the engine company is making a determined advance, ladder personnel should ladder the building, open upper story windows and search all rooms they can enter. As the search is made, ventilation is begun in all heavily charged areas of the building. Partitions, ceiling spaces, stair soffits, cockloft and attic spaces must be carefully examined.

## MANSIONS

In an ordinary size home that is structurally sound, there are no acceptable excuses for failure to pursue an aggressive interior attack. However, in mansions, the area may be so large and the fire so extensive that an interior attack may fail. The inaccessibility of some mansions to fire department apparatus and the limited water supply may foredoom them to complete fire involvement.

In these situations, the limited water supply is first used judiciously to cover rescue operations and then to prevent the extension of fire to adjacent buildings—and even to brush, shrubs and trees when they are tinder-dry. Laddermen should raise ladders, search accessible rooms, and make every effort to completely evacuate the building. An 1½-inch line may have to be taken up a ladder to protect a searching party.

In some instances, works of art, priceless antiques and other valuables can be salvaged from these buildings. The fire can travel through partitions and extend to the gable towers cupolas, attics and mansard roof areas. Limited water and manpower may not permit offensive operations. In this case, fire fighters may provide the best service by controlling the fire as best they can and removing valuables and furnishings.

## ATTACHED ONE AND TWO-FAMILY RESIDENCES

Generally, attached one and two-family dwellings have a common cockloft, or space, between the top floor ceiling and the roof deck. Also, the first floor beams rest on the foundation, abutting or overlapping the beams of the adjoining building. Where the floor beams rest upon a girder on the second and higher floors, it is likely that no fire stopping will be found between the floor beams in the division wall. These deficiencies will allow fire to spread rapidly from one building to another, at the cellar, upper floor and cockloft levels.

Therefore, ladder personnel must make a quick examination of adjoining areas of attached buildings for any extension of fire. If fire should run the partitions in division walls, the ceilings of all floors must be opened for examination on both sides of the party wall.

## FRAME TENEMENTS

Serious as are the hazards of the attached one and two-family frame residences, they are dwarfed considerably when compared to frame tenements. These buildings are usually three or four stories high and may be in a continuous row, often running the length of a city block. In addition to concealed spaces between floors and ceilings and a common cockloft, we also find the following channels for fire spread:

1. Light and vent shafts. These can occur between two buildings and are generally about midway along the sides. Such shafts vary in area from 15 to 60 square feet and have two or more windows opening into the shaft from each floor of the two buildings. Some buildings have open shafts, which open to the rear yard for their entire height. The enclosed shaft is much more hazardous than the open shaft as a channel for fire spread.

2. Water closet air shaft. Small casement windows or louvers in the partition provide ventilation to water closets from the shaft at each floor.

3. Dumbwaiter shafts. These are enclosed and serve each floor.

4. Sliding doors. A hollow space within the partitions containing the doors provide a horizontal channel through which fire can extend from one apartment to the other and then vertically to floors above.

5. Interior stairways in pairs of adjoining row buildings extend side by side, separated by the division wall. At each floor, open horizontal spaces may extend from one building to the other at the stairway platform level. Though some of these spaces in the division wall may be brick-filled, the bricks are laid loosely, and fire and hot gasses can and do extend through these spaces.

6. Ornamental cornices of wood construction are often present in these buildings, extending along the roof for the entire length of the row. Store cornices, of similar construction, also provide horizontal spaces to convey fire from one building to another.

Modern building codes provide for fire-stopping cornices and division walls. But this is often ineffective because of faulty workmanship. It is obvious that fire-stopping can not be depended upon and fire can spread rapidly from lower to upper levels and from building to building. There are other avenues by which fire can spread, such as hot-air ducts and registers, air conditioning ducts and the enclosures for water and gas pipes. If you have a major fire in any section of a wood frame tenement building, anticipate spread to higher floors as well as to adjoining buildings.

## MAJOR FIRES IN COCKLOFTS

Hose lines must be stretched to the top floor of the adjoining buildings, as well as in the fire building, when there is a major fire in a cockloft. The roof in the fire building must be cut over the hottest portion of the fire. Ceilings in both the fire building and the adjoining buildings must be pulled to expose and extinguish the fire.

Cutting a hole in a roof for ventilation may at times be a difficult task. When first erected, these buildings frequently had tin roofs, but through the years, layers of roofing paper and tar were applied over the tin to keep the roof watertight. The layers of tar can be so thick that tools will bind in this mass.

Consequently, the job can be slow and tedious, and an impatient chief may resort to pulling ceilings in the fire and adjoining buildings before the cockloft has been ventilated. This is a crucial error, for as the hot gases mix with the new-found oxygen, fire may travel along row buildings from one to another until the entire cockloft space becomes a mass of fire.

When ignition occurs, gases expand greatly in volume and tend to vent themselves at any opening. Therefore, as the ceilings continue to be pulled, the fire will use these openings as vent points. This can result in chasing the men from the top floor. Furthermore, once the tar starts burning, heavy black smoke will pour from the ceiling openings. The chief, now forced into a defensive operation, must resort to using heavy exterior streams. The situation is further aggravated by the fact that the roof has become too weak to support men working on it. The chief must now wait until the fire burns through the roof before resuming an offensive operation.

## CONGESTED FRAMES

Up to now, we have discussed fires in individual frame buildings and fires extending in common cockloft spaces in adjoining buildings. In most communities, there are congested older districts with frame buildings. The spacing between the individual buildings is usually narrow, and fire can travel rapidly from building to building.

To give consideration to this problem, there will be a discussion of an actual fire. The description of the fire situation will follow closely the events that actually took place at this particular fire.

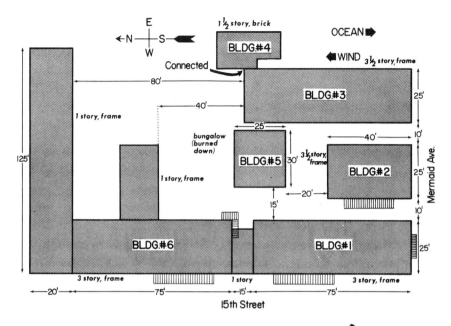

Figure 1. *Plan view of congested frame structures involved in a serious fire situation.*

## FIRE SITUATION—CONGESTED FRAME BUILDINGS (Figure 1)

*DESCRIPTION*

Building 1 is a three-story frame lodging house with a frontage of approximately 25 feet on Mermaid Ave. and 75 feet on 15th St. On the first floor there are two stores, a butcher and luggage shop. There are fire escapes on both the Mermaid Ave. and 15th St. sides. The entrance to the lodging house portion is at the northerly end of the building on 15th St. The wooden stairs are unenclosed and lead to a long narrow hallway through the center of the building in a north-south direction. The stairs and hallways are protected by an automatic sprinkler system connected to a city main.

Building 2 is a 3½-story frame structure, about 25 X 40 feet, with a tropical fish store on the first floor and a rooming house on the upper floors. The wooden stairs and hallway are not enclosed, but they are protected by an automatic sprinkler system the same as in Building 1. On the west side of the building, there is a fire escape to all floors that terminates in the alley.

Building 3 is similar in construction to Building 2. However, it is occupied by only two families; the stairway is not protected by a sprinkler system.

Building 4 is a 1$^{1}/_{2}$-story modern brick dwelling. It is set back about 20 feet from Neptune Ave. and is contiguous to the rear of Building 3.

Building 5 is a five-room frame bungalow burned to the ground so no other description can be given.

Building 6 which is similar in construction to Building 1, has an open wooden balcony across the south side of the third floor. There is a one-story sign-painting store, 15 feet wide, attached to Buildings 1 and 6, leaving a 15-foot space between the two larger buildings above the first floor.

Building 6 has a one-story extension of dilapidated, frame construction with a 20-foot street frontage and a depth of about 125 feet. It is occupied by a restaurant.

This section of the city is serviced by a low pressure water system. The hydrant spacing is extremely good. For example, there is a hydrant in front of the fire building and another on 15th street opposite the sign-painting store.

*WIND*

There is a brisk wind of 20 to 25 mph, blowing from the south.

*TRANSMITTAL OF ALARM*

Fire is discovered by a tenant of Building 3. He runs to the nearby firehouse, but the personnel are operating at a four-alarm fire elsewhere. He then runs to the corner and pulls a fire alarm box.

1. Fire very likely started in Building 5 or in the open space between Buildings 2 and 5 because it entered the rooms of Building 2 from the rear and spread from room to room, as well as upward. The sprinkler in the hallway and stairs operated satisfactorily, for the stairs remain intact, although the rear of the building is gutted.
2. Extension to Building 1—There is an alley of about 10 feet between Buildings 1 and 2. There are many windows on all floors in both buildings along this alleyway. The fire quickly communicated to the roof space of Building 1 and also to a room on the top floor in the rear. The sprinkler in Building 1 kept fire from breaking out in the stairs and hallway. The siding is burning on both buildings.
3. Extension to Building 3—The alleyway between Buildings 2 and 3 is approximately 10 feet wide. There are many windows in both buildings on this alleyway. The fire is consuming the siding of both buildings and has communicated to stairs of Building 3. It later breaks out in top floor rooms on the east side.
4. Extension to Building 6—The siding on the rear of this building is beginning to burn, but the fire does not enter the interior to any extent.

*ARRIVAL OF UNITS*

Because of a four-alarm fire in the area, the initial response consists of an engine, a ladder and a battalion chief. Another ladder company stops to assist while returning from the fourth alarm.

*CONDITIONS ON ARRIVAL OF FIRST DUE UNITS*

Fire has complete possession of Building 2 except for the store on the first floor. Flames are shooting from all windows —front and side and rear—on all floors above the first. There are no tenants at any windows.

Building 5 is completely engulfed in flames and practically consumed.

In Building 1, about 10 people are at various windows awaiting rescue. The heat and heavy smoke make it very difficult for the firemen to operate from the front of the building. Nevertheless, all these people are rescued. Fire is in the roof space and all of the siding on the east side is aflame.

In Building 3, the fire is burning vigorously along siding on the west side and has entered the stairwell. One person is rescued from this building.

Most of the occupants were led to safety from Building 6 before the arrival of the fire department.

### FIRE FIGHTING PROBLEMS AND SOLUTIONS

There were 10 people awaiting rescue from Building 1. The heat was so intense that a fireman had great difficulty gaining access to the balcony of the fire escape on the Mermaid Ave. side of the building. Two lines were stretched to cover the alleyway between Buildings 1 and 2. Because of the shortage of manpower, many civilians were pressed into service to expedite line movement. By getting the water between the fire and the occupants, the rescue of the 10 people could proceed expeditiously and safely.

Figure 2. *A deckpipe stream was directed over roof of 1-story "sign" store and over roof of Building 1, to darken fire in rear and reduce heat so a hand line could be placed on rear fire escape of Building 6.*

When the second engine company arrived, the men operated a deck pipe and directed the stream over the one-story sign store extension and the roof of Building 1 to hit Building 5 and the rear of Building 2. In addition, they stretched a hand line to the balcony of Building 6. (Figure 2)

When the third engine company arrived, its men were able to cover the extension by way of the alley between Buildings 2 and 3 and to reduce the intensity of fire in Building 2, as well as to extinguish fire in Building 3.

As subsequent companies arrived, the critical positions were reinforced and lines were taken into individual buildings to complete extinguishment. The fire was côntrolled and extinguished without significant spread, for it was largely confined to the stage of development it had attained at the time of arrival of the first engine company.

## *QUESTIONS*

*1. Five lives were lost in Building 2. Why weren't the first two engine and ladder companies assigned to darken the fire and rescue the occupants?*

2. *Would 1½-inch hose be an effective weapon in the early stages of this fire to protect the trapped occupants and prevent major extension of the fire?*

3. *In Building 1, there were 10 people awaiting rescue. They were in their rooms and at windows. Sprinklers were operating in the stairs and hallways. There was no fire in the stairs or hallways. Explain why the trapped tenants did not escape by these arteries.*

4. *The second engine operated a deck pipe and directed the stream over the roof of Building 1 and over the one-story sign building to the fire area, hitting Building 5 and the rear of Building 2. What were the advantages of this tactical procedure?*

5. *The first three engine companies were discharging about 2000 gpm. The hydrant spacing was excellent and the water supply adequate. The stretches were short and the streams were operational quickly. Now, presume that the water supply was inadequate, able to supply only two 2½-inch lines. Where would you position these lines and why?*

*ANSWERS*

1. When forces are limited and the fire situation is extensive, rescue operations are concentrated on doing what will help the most people. With fire showing from all windows of Building 2, there is little, if any, chance of rescues. On the other hand, there are 10 people endangered in Building 1, and if lines are not immediately positioned between them and the fire, rescue work will become almost impossible. The deck pipe stream from 15th St. and the line from the balcony of Building 6 reduced the heat and expedited the rescues.

It is an essential of command procedures at fires that when operating with few companies and limited personnel, you must make a decision as to what can and can not be done—what is possible and what is impossible. Even if the first two engine companies were assigned to fight their way to the upper floors of Building 2 and the ladder company to ladder, search and evacuate Building 2, they would have been unable to accomplish any rescues from Building 2. Such activity would have sacrificed the ten people who were rescued from Building 1.

2. The size of the hose line must be selected with regard to the amount of fire it has to extinguish. There must be a sufficient mass of water to absorb all the Btu generated by the burning wooden structure. Stream impact and reach is of vital significance at this fire. A 1¹/₂-inch stream lacks the three important qualities for extinguishing a fire of this magnitude— massive cooling, impact and reach.

   Therefore, for massive fires, the tactician will use master stream appliances and, for mobility, 2¹/₂-inch lines.

3. When sprinklers operate in such a situation, smoke is cooled and lacks buoyancy. Under these conditions, ventilation is ineffective. Although there is no flame, the density of the smoke can make these escape arteries practically impassible.

4. Advantages:
   a. Quick water was directed on a large body of fire. A deck pipe is operational within a minute with a hydrant so convenient.
   b. It takes only one man to operate a deck pipe.
   c. It will discharge 500–600 gallons of water per minute. Massive fire requires the use of massive streams.
   d. Diminishing the heat made it practical to position a 2¹/₂-inch line on the balcony of Building 6. This line then was able to extinguish fire in the siding of Buildings 6 and 1 and to increase the flow of water toward Buildings 2 and 5.

5. In the alleyway between Buildings 1 and 2. Reason: Since resources are limited, your tactics should be based on the concept of doing the greatest good for the greatest number. By positioning the lines in the alleyway, you make it possible to rescue the 10 persons trapped in Building 1.


**FRAME BUILDINGS—CONTIGUOUS**

There are nine connected two-story frame buildings. The fire originates on the first floor of the center dwelling. The smoke, heat and flames have already spread in volume up the stairway and to a number of rooms on the second floor. The people have already been evacuated from all nine buildings. The cockloft and cornices are continuous; there is no fire-stopping. (Figure 3)

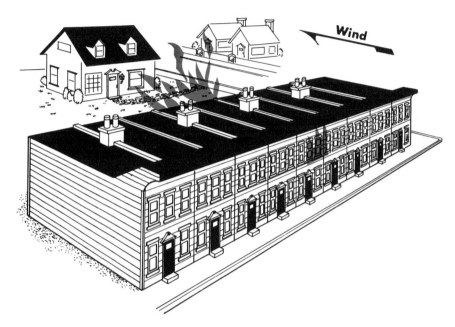

Figure 3.   *The immediate action by the fire department determines whether this fire is confined or spreads throughout this row of residences.*

*QUESTIONS*

*1. Where would you position the first hose line, and why?*

2. *Suppose the first line stretched was 1¹/₂-inch hose and the fire was beyond its quenching effects, where would you position the second hose line?*

3. *With the amount of fire described, what is your prediction of the condition of the cockloft area?*

4. *But is the fire roaring in the cockloft?*

5. *Are these superheated gases an advantage or disadvantage from a firemanic viewpoint?*

6. *Suppose the roof was intact and the ceilings at the top floor of buildings 4 and 6 were pulled, what could you anticipate?*

7. *It is well established that the first opening should be made in the roof of the fire building, as directly over the fire as possible. Is it advisable to use this opening for stream penetration?*

1. The first line should be positioned to attack the fire at its point of origin. There may be a tendency to use this line in adjoining buildings to cut off fire extension. This can lead to chasing the fire. By hitting the original fire and moving up the stairway in the fire building, you diminish a great amount of heat and reduce the extension possibilities. Even if the fire does extend, it will be easier to cope with this extension if the main body of fire has been darkened.

2. The second hose line would be assigned to the fire building. One of these lines must move to the second floor to extinguish fire in the stairwell and to darken fire in the various rooms. The other line must complete the extinguishment of fire on the first floor and protect men operating on second floor.

   If the original two lines were stretched to the adjacent frame buildings, their positions would become untenable since the intensity of fire in the original building would increase rapidly. The longer the original fire burns without the quenching effects of water, the greater the probability of losing all nine buildings.

   Exterior streams for this type structure have very limited effectiveness because of the room partitions in such residences. Therefore, offensive operations must be vigorously pursued from the outset.

   Exposure protection takes precedence over confinement only when the life hazard is a factor or when confinement becomes an impossible condition.

3. There is no doubt that the superheated gases have permeated the entire cockloft.

4. The drawing shows no roof openings and the ceilings are intact. You can expect that there is insufficient oxygen to support rapid, flaming combustion.

5. It depends upon your strategy and tactics. These gases actually act as a suppressant to the fire. They become dangerous only if you allow oxygen to mix with the gases. If this occurs, you have lost all nine buildings. For example, if you cut the roof over Building 1, the gases will combine with the atmospheric oxygen and you will witness roaring combustion at the roof opening, similar to that from an oxyacetylene torch. As these gases emerge, they will be replaced by some oxygen and in effect you will have caused the spread of the fire throughout the cockloft.

6. By pulling the ceilings in the adjoining building before opening the roof in the fire building, you permit the entrance of new oxygen which will mix with the hot gases. This will increase the volume of the fire, and as the volume of gases increases, the new openings may well become vent points. This can result in the men being chased from their top floor positions. Furthermore, if the roof tar starts burning, heavy black smoke will pour from these ceiling openings. This may force the chief into defensive operations.

7. The hole in the roof is used for ventilation. To insert a nozzle into this opening would considerably impede the flow of gases outward.

   After the gases in the cockloft have been vented by opening up the roof, then the ceilings in the adjoining building should be examined and opened if necessary.

   Do not hesitate to open up concealed spaces. The risk of rapid extensive fire spread warrants the small damage required to assure proper confinement.

*Chapter 13*

# Church Fires

The old-type cathedrals or the large non-fireproof churches constitute one of the most serious exposure problems faced by the chiefs of our many communities and cities throughout the nation. They are a more serious problem than lumberyards, since they are generally in the built-up sections of communities while lumberyards are often on the periphery of the communities.

## USUALLY A TOTAL LOSS

It has been stated in publications that a major fire in an old-type church or other similar religious building will usually result in a total loss. What are the built-in weaknesses that cause such a pessimistic outlook? Why must an experienced fire chief stand in front of an edifice of architectural beauty and preside at its destruction while experiencing anguish and frustration as each successive fire stage tolls the eventual outcome?

From the simple we can often understand the complex. The chief arriving at a moderate size fire in a small church of 200 seating capacity will coordinate his forces and generally succeed in preserving the major portion of the building. He will direct his line or lines through a favorable entrance, select and time his roof and side ventilation, sweep his stream against the ceiling over the fire area and swiftly open the ceiling and side walls where fire may have entered concealed spaces. The fire is rapidly brought under control and damage is minimal. Does the same strategy apply when a moderate fire is encountered in an old-type cathedral with a seating capacity of 2,000 persons?

The strategy of fighting fires in old, large, non-fireproof places of worship is essentially the same as that proposed for a small church. Failure results not from a difference in strategy but the inability to carry out the tactical operations required to assure success. The entrance to the fire in the small church is now through high oak doors. The localized fire and heat is replaced by a formidable temperature similar to that encountered in a pier fire. The smoke and heat at ceiling level is capable of a smoke explosion of tremendous proportion. The roof, which was so simply opened by a few laddermen, is now 80 feet high, formed by one-inch planking, covered with a slate or tile, and pitched at an angle of 45 degrees.

The ceilings which were so readily pulled with 10 or 12-foot hooks is now 60 or more feet above the floor and fashioned in dome or other design which permits a general, dust-filled, open space or cockloft between the ceiling and the roof deck. The non-firestopped vertical openings, cleverly concealed to enhance the esthetic interior design, run from the basement to the open roof area at ceiling level and will allow fire to enter an area containing an amount of wood normally found in a small lumberyard.

The principal reason why a chief cannot generally control a well advanced church fire is the inability to ventilate the roof area. Enough doors and windows are usually available for access, proper ventilation and eventual control of a fire in the church proper, but openings to roof spaces are fewer and less accessible. Where there are insufficient windows, doors, scuttles or skylights to relieve smoke and heat at the roof level, it is advisable to raise aerial ladders in an endeavor to cut openings in the roof. Where physical difficulties prevent this form of roof attack, the hot gases accumulating under the roof will ignite and expand to involve the entire roof area. The violence of this development may cause a sudden collapse of the roof, or the introduction of oxygen from ceiling failure may intensify the fire so fiercely that it shortens the period of time before structural failure.

Where the fire has developed in a cockloft and direct accessibility and ventilation cannot be attained, the chief must cover the exposures and prepare for possible collapse. He may hope that the roof sheathing will be of light construction and that the fire will vent itself locally before full lateral spread occurs, but he is no longer the master of this situation and must accept a defensive position. Time is working against him and the condition will continue to deteriorate.

Despite the gloom predicted, the astute chief will not accept failure until he has assured himself that he has not overlooked some vital opportunity. Ingenuity and persistence are required in the early stages. Acceptance and caution are required when the fire is well advanced.

The following cases are offered to emphasize some of the difficulties at typical church fires. Some conclude in success, some in failure, but each points up the factors that led to the individual outcome.

## CASE 1 (Figure 1)

Early in the morning of October 19, 1956, Boston fire fighters performed the difficult feat of stopping a well-advanced fire in Holy Trinity Cathedral. The building was 75 feet wide, 200 feet deep and nearly 100 feet high. The fire originated in the rear basement and extended to the upper church at the organ and then into the choir loft, the bell tower and the concealed space between the under side of the roof and the main church ceiling.

The immediate size-up indicated that heavy smoke was in the basement and fire was extending to the first floor. There was no

**Figure 1.** *This fire was controlled because of offensive operations within the church. Fortunately the roof had scuttle openings for ventilation; lines could be advanced up the ladders to the various lofts of the church. The deluge set provided the needed stream reach.*

direct stairway from the first floor to the basement, which was divided into two separate sections.

Using a battering ram to force a basement door and to gain access to the first floor, lines were stretched swiftly to both areas and one of the first floor lines was taken to the choir loft area. A 100-foot aerial was raised to ventilate by removing large scuttles on one side of the roof and an 85-foot aerial was raised to the other side. An additional line was used to augment the difficult cellar operation. Additional help was summoned to increase the interior attack, provide replacements for members overcome in the basement and to prepare for exposure protection.

It was learned that the interior bell tower could be reached from the roof and that access to the critical roof space area was near this location. These fortunate features, coupled with the removal of the roof scuttles, provided a chance to continue the interior attack and control the fire in the roof space.

Engine companies on the second alarm stretched two additional lines to the basement, two lines to two upper level lofts, and a line via an aerial to a third level loft. They also set up a deluge set in front of the building. Two ladder companies on the second alarm raised additional aerials to the roof to assist in ventilation and also provided extension ladders within the church to assist in maintaining access to the loft regions.

Despite the fact that fire was breaking through the large front windows, heavy smoke was issuing from the belfry, fire was in the hanging ceiling, and men were being overcome in the cellar, it was decided to press the interior attack and avoid the use of exterior streams.

Third alarm units stretched two additional lines up aerials to operate at the roof level, used a portable gun in the choir loft to increase the effectiveness of the stream, placed more ladders and emergency lights within the church and relieved at basement positions.

As the crucial turning point of control was reached, smaller lines were introduced to extend positions and provide needed flexibility for pursuit of the fire. Precautionary lines connected to deck pipes and ladder pipes were never used and the fire was controlled with a total financial loss of $70,000, most of which was attributable to the organ damage.

This church was saved from major structural damage because of the availability of vent facilities and the aggressive advancement of hose lines while ventilation was proceeding. The decision to withhold exterior streams permitted a one-sided attack at all levels. The fire was being driven back toward the front of the church and being confined from horizontal spread. Ventilation at the roof controlled the vertical spread, prevented horizontal roof spread and permitted the units to advance and follow up their successes at each level. The full utilization of manpower and equipment provided the essential venting that turned the tide at this fire.

## CASE 2 (Figure 2)

In a church in New York City, fire gained great headway in the basement. The street on which the church fronted was dense with smoke and heat conditions in the auditorium were so severe that fire fighters could not enter. Hot gases surging from a basement doorway burst into flame as they mixed with the exterior air. There were window openings at the rear of the basement.

The battalion chief in charge of this fire ordered the three engine companies to stretch 2½-inch lines to the front of the church. When the streams were in readiness, the three lines moved simultaneously into the basement.

The activities of the two ladder companies were coordinated with this line advancement. The first ladder company was instructed to open or break all rear basement windows while the engine companies were starting their advance. The second ladder company raised its aerial to provide roof ventilation. Most fortunately, they found windows at dormers. When these were opened or broken, the men were met with such a rush of heat, that they had to quickly move from a catwalk back to the aerial.

Now it was possible to enter the main church. The fire had not burned through the flooring to any measurable degree and the first floor partitions were relatively cool. The fire was soon under control.

This church was saved from major structural damage because of the availability of venting facilities and aggressive advancement of hose lines while ventilation was proceeding. These are exactly the same reasons why the Boston fire fighters were able to save Holy Trinity Cathedral.

We have considered church fires where the strategy worked. To present a fuller scope of this picture, it would be worthwhile to review a church fire which resulted in total loss.

Figure 2. *Firemen are advancing 3 lines simultneously. Fire is venting out the basement rear. Adequate roof ventilation permitted quick extinguishment.*

## CASE 3 (Figure 3)

This fire occurred on Dec. 20, 1963, with the temperature near zero. The church was 67 x 144 feet and 100 feet high. It was built in 1867 and had all the construction defects common to old, large churches.

Figure 3. *6 or 7 floors of the adjacent multiple dwelling were simultaneously exposed to heavy fire. The need for handlines in the multiple dwelling was so great the stand pipe system was overtaxed, necessitating direct stretches from the street.*

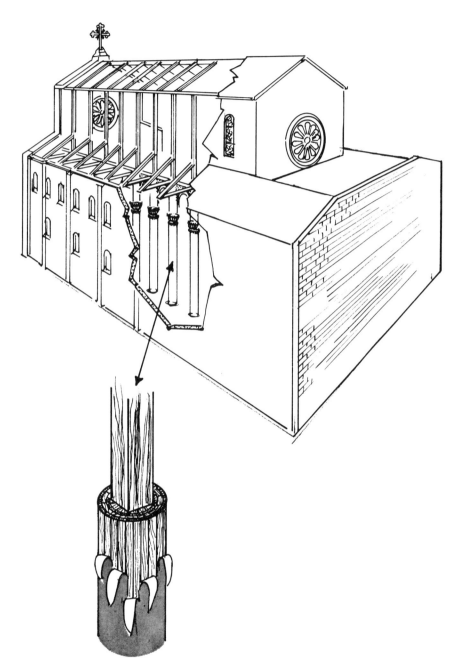

Figure 4. *Cutaway exposes the forest of wood in what otherwise appears to be a fire resistive structure.*

This fire had an inauspicious origin in a confessional booth. Since the booth was wood and the drapes flammable, fire did not take long to spread. It rapidly involved the balcony, choir and organ loft. Before the arrival of the fire forces, it had penetrated into concealed ceiling areas and three attic spaces.

The first-arriving engine company had to fight its way into the church because of the intensity of fire at the door. The second line was stretched up the stairs to the choir and organ loft. Fire fighters struggled to get a large capacity deluge set into operation at the main aisle of the church. Other companies were now arriving and there seemed to be ,a splendid opportunity to continue the offensive attack within the church.

However, the ladder companies could find no openings in the roof, and it was impracticable to attempt to cut the roof because of the darkness, sloped surfaces, height and icy conditions. Therefore, the attic spaces were never properly ventilated (Figure 4). The interior attack was abondoned, exterior streams were directed from exposed buildings and the collapse of the roof was anticipated. The roof disintegration remained as the last problem. Would the huge covering fall in a monolithic mass, carrying sections of wall with it and showering the exposures with a sudden release of heat and brands? Fortunately, this did not occur. The massive roof burned off in small sections and fell gracefully within the confines of the four-wall enclosure.

*CRITIQUE*

This complete destruction of one of the great landmarks of a city must be attributed to a fault in the design and construction of the building and the lack of built-in fire protection facilities. Inability to provide any form of roof ventilation forebode the failure of interior attack and the ultimate loss of the structure.

## CASE 4 (Figure 5)

In the midmorning of a clear day in August, a ladder company in midtown was directed to respond to what was enigmatically described as a "small fire in the roof of a church." Welders repairing damaged copper flashing at the base of a pitched section of roof had ignited the under portion of the roof. The fire then ascended to the peak at the rear of the building.

The church was about 175 feet deep and was irregular in width. The main section was about 125 feet wide, reduced to 75 feet at the first roof level and terminated in a steeply pitched slate roof rising to about 100 feet. First-arriving units reportèd that the attic space was not accessible from the lower church, but there was a small rose window at the front of the attic and a few covered scuttles at the base of the pitched roof. A utility company had cut a trench in the street at the front of the building, restricting approach of apparatus to that location. The three other sides were inaccessible for the close approach of fire apparatus.

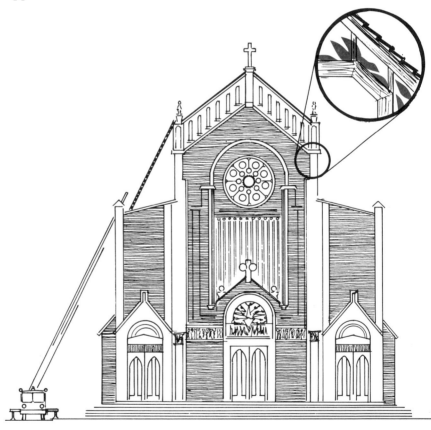

Figure 5. *This fire was an evolution in laddering. The aerial reached only the 1st roof level, necessitating 35' ladders for further elevation.*

As the first aerial ladder reached only to the base of the first roof level and time would be required to stretch lines, the deputy chief directed a large outside stream in through the rose window to hold the fire in the rear portion of the attic. Lines were stretched and 35-foot ground ladders were hoisted to the first roof and raised to the base of the pitched roof. At this point, operations were restricted. Roof ladders were insufficient in length and the slate roof was difficult to climb as individual slates might slide out from under the footing of a climber. In addition, slates fell and endangered fire personnel.

It was impossible to cut the roof at a high point over the fire. When lines were in position, a few available scuttles were broken. Located near the base of the pitched roof, the scuttles failed to ventilate the high point and allowed more oxygen to enter the roof space. However, they were of some value in that they permitted water to enter the burning area.

An examination of the interior of the church revealed that heavy fire remained in the attic space and that the ceilings were intact. There was one hazard in the main church. Some lights, hung from the attic and anchored to machinery there, fell to the church floor.

After a relatively short time, a curved portion of the apse roof over the altar slid into the year yard and vented the roof. As further sections of the roof burned through and vented the cockloft, the hose lines became effective and extinguished the fire.

Entering the fire area, examination revealed the features that had contributed to final extinguishment. The roof sheathing boards were comparatively light for this type of roof and the domed ceiling construction was of heavy reinforced concrete. The strong ceiling resisted the fire and the weak roof covering permitted eventual venting.

*CRITIQUE*

The construction of the roof area was the key factor in final control. The chief utilized the few advantages he had. His early direction of a stream through the rose window confined the fire to the rear; his careful venting at lower levels of the pitched roof afforded some degree of water penetration. Nevertheless, he was at the mercy of the features of construction. In this case, the roof was weak and the ceilings strong. In most cases, the roof is heavy and the domed ceilings are much less capable of withstanding sustained heat. In some cases, workmen performing repair in an attic drop sharp tools which penetrate the ceiling and fall to the church floor.

This particular fire emphasizes the need for local companies to be familiar with the inner design of a church and to develop a pre-fire plan of operations.

## CASE 5

A large, old, brick church with an open beam ceiling, many concealed spaces and a sharply pitched roof became involved in fire. The original fire spread to the area below the open roof beams. Because of the presence of side area setbacks, the ladder company could not place its aerial parallel to the pitched side of the roof. While efforts were being made to place large deluge sets within the church to sweep the ceiling area, a terrific smoke explosion took place. Like a typical backdraft, hot smoke and gases accumulated under the roof and suddenly ignited. As these gases reached the outside and combined with oxygen, the spires of flames could be seen for miles. The explosion caused the organ loft to buckle and fall, and blasted loose a 21-foot section of a contiguous convent roof.

*CRITIQUE*

Once again, the inadequacy of venting facilities at roof level proved disastrous to a church.

## CASE 6

A non-fireproof church was built in 1893, 50 X 100 feet and 80 feet high. The fire spread with great rapidity, and at 3:09 p.m., before the arrival of the first alarm units, the church was a mass of flame. Within minutes of the arrival of the first units, a back draft erupted and propelled great masses of flames up the large inner court of exposure 2. Nine floors of a multiple dwelling were in serious jeopardy. Minutes later, the roof of the church collapsed and drove heat and flames across a wide street to crack windows on all floors of exposure 1.

*EXPOSURE #2*

Protection of exposures 1 and 3 required a major assignment of companies, but the paramount problem was exposure 2. The wind was from the southwest at 13 mph with gusts to 21 mph. The narrow court acted as a chimney. Fire entered two apartments on the exposed court on each of the nine floors. Each floor had a major fire. The standpipe riser was only 4 inches in diameter. Engine companies fed the system through the siamese inlets and through a number of floor outlets. Lines used to extinguish the fires on the first through fourth floors were hand-stretched from the street. Other hand lines were hoisted up the exterior of the building with roof ropes and hose rollers. The heat condition within this building was so severe that masks were essential and units had to be relieved at frequent intervals.

*CRITIQUE*

When large, non-fireproof churches adjoin other tall structures, the entire area is imperiled. In this fire, the church was lost before the companies left the firehouse. A chief would need 20 to 30 engine companies and 5 to 10 ladder companies to successfully cope with the life and exposure problems. The fire units must be located so that they can reach the scene in a relatively short time. Not too many of our cities are prepared to furnish manpower and equipment in such abundance and within a time span of 5 to 20 minutes.

The chief lesson to be learned from this fire, therefore, is one of fire protection rather than one of fire fighting. Tall structures should not be erected on lot lines adjoining large-area, non-fireproof structures. Even if the high rise structure were fully protected with an automatic sprinkler system, the hazard would be too severe, for no sprinkler system has been designed to protect nine floors simultaneously from an exposure fire.

It is evident from the cases described that little can be done to save a non-fireproof church unless the fire is discovered in its early stages or successful roof ventilation can be accomplished.

When an interior attack can be made, it must be made vigorously with full use of breathing equipment, fog and solid streams, and the use of large nozzles to reach high ceiling areas. If the fire is localized, every effort should be made to confine it to the area of involvement. Where fire is blowing out windows on one side or portion of the church, try to approach from the opposite side and drive the fire out of the building. It will be difficult to resist the use of exterior streams, but such resistance is essential to the success of the interior attack. Move only in one direction and produce ventilation above and ahead of line advancement. The problem of roof ventilation is the key to success. If possible, one of the chief officers should be assigned to the coordination of this single task.

Greater alarms must be transmitted at the early stages of major fires in churches. Despite the fact that an interior attack may prevail, the defensive operations must be arranged. Exposures are generally present in the form of other buildings associated with the church. Enough companies must be on hand to perform these defensive operations without weakening the interior attack. In addition, the difficulties presented at roof level will require the presence of many aerial ladders and sufficient personnel to ventilate the roof area.

Automatic sprinkler systems provide the best means for controlling church fires, but it is fantasy to expect church officials to install a fully automatic sprinkler system in their old-type cathedrals. However, discussions with church officials can at times reach accord on adequate fire protection. For example, many fires start in the sacristy or other small rooms adjoining the main body of a church. Fires, of course, also originate in the basement. Since the pressure in the public water mains is generally adequate to feed sprinkler systems in cellar and first floor levels, these installations are quite reasonable. If, in addition, automatic roof vents and fire detection systems are installed, disasters in these landmark edifices can become rare.

The following questions and answers will assist the student to bring into a more definite form the strategy and tactics of managing a major church fire.

*1. Summarize the principal points involved in attacking a major fire which originates in the basement of a typical non-fireproof large church.*

*2. State the principal reason from a fire fighting aspect why a well advanced church fire invariably results in total destruction.*

3. *Where there are no available doors, scuttles or skylights to immediately effect roof ventilation would it be advisable to concentrate ladder personnel in an endeavor to cut major opening in roof?*

4. *Since roof ventilation is of prime importance, why then is it not accomplished at all major church fires?*

5. *What happens when the roof is not adequately opened?*

6. *Some modern churches do not have a cockloft. Yet their ceilings are high and the roof is unpierced. What strategy may be feasible to dissipate the heat accumulating at the underside of the ceiling?*

1. *Basement Operations*
   A. If fire is blowing out windows, do not change its direction.
   B. If wind is a factor, try to work so that it is on the backs of the men as they move in.
   C. Use breathing apparatus, fog nozzles and solid streams.
   D. Effect ventilation as enginemen move toward fire.
   E. If men are moving in from one end of the church, it is essential that there be adequate ventilation at the other end of the church.
   F. Move in only from one direction.
   G. Do not use any exterior streams.
   H. Open ceilings as soon as possible.
   I. The major goal is to coordinate ventilation with line advancement. This means ventilation from above as well as horizontally.
   *Roof Operations*
   A. Aerials and elevated platforms to roof. (Figure 6)
   B. Originally concentrate as many laddermen as possible at the roof area.

C. Find every available means of ventilating—doors, scuttles, skylights, windows, dormers, roof exhausts, etc.
D. Where conditions permit, vent as directly above the fire as possible.
E. Vent as near the roof peak as possible.
F. Where there are no existing means of venting, try to pierce the roofing material.
G. Assign a chief to this area to coordinate movement of personnel and to press for ventilation.

Figure 6.  *The new elevated platforms and power saws improve chances of piercing church roofs.*

*First Floor Operations*

A. Advance hand lines into the church.
B. Use distributors and cellar pipes if practicable and if basement lines cannot advance.
C. Set up interior deluge streams beneath masonry arches.
D. Laddermen will ventilate and open concealed spaces.
E. If no other alternative, flood wooden floors.

*Outside Operations*

A. Set up an exterior defense while interior fire operations are in progress.
B. This calls for early transmission of sufficient greater alarms to man equipment for the surrounding of the fire.
C. Use no major exterior streams while there is a chance for the interior attack to progress.

2. The inability to effectively ventilate the roof.

3. A. There is no other alternative.
   B. If roof ventilation is not effected, the church will be lost

4. A. Peaked roofs entail dangerous operating conditions.
   B. Aerial ladders cannot generally be positioned to parallel the pitch of the roof and provide a safe working base.
   C. Roof ladders are totally inadequate.
   D. Heavy slate is quite difficult to remove and will fall and scale when loosened, posing a hazard below.
   E. Then there is the problem of cutting through roof boards from precarious perches.
   F. Smoke conditions will be severe.
   G. We are not adequately tooled to accomplish the mission.

5. A. The hot gases will accumulate directly under the roof.
   B. In time, they will ignite.
   C. It is not necessary that all the gases be mixed with the proper amount of oxygen and at sufficient intensity of temperature.

D. The sudden expansion of gases due to ignition will cause a sufficient buildup of pressure to drop the ceiling.

E. When supplied with additional oxygen, the fire rages, feeding upon wooden structural members and the dust deposits of decades.

F. The roof will soon collapse.

6. A. Use three or four deluge sets to sweep the underside of the ceiling.

B. Use high pressures.

*Chapter 14*

# *Cellar Fires*

An experienced chief officer accepts one of his greatest challenges when he encounters heat and smoke belching from the cellar of an unsprinklered, non-fireproof building. The upper stories of the building are sitting on a sea of flames and time is working against him. Unless control can be established within a reasonable time, the fire will surely find channels to the upper floors. Fortunately, one of two factors which reduce the seriousness of the commonly encountered cellar fire is generally present.

The first factor is that many cellar fires have not developed sufficient heat upon discovery to prevent a direct offensive attack. With self-contained breathing equipment, properly trained engine company personnel can usually descend through the upper layer of moderate heat and advance at floor level to the seat of the developing fire. Ladder companies can usually provide ventilation sufficient to carry off the moderate heat and smoke, including the added smoke and steam developed when water actually contacts the fire.

The second factor mitigating the hazard is that many are "cellar" fires in name only. One or more of the sides of the building foundation are partially or wholly above grade, and direct ventilation and access are possible to some extent. After the first line is positioned to prevent extension to the upper floors, an additional line, or lines, can be used from the more favorable above-grade openings in the foundation. A rapid survey will reveal these spots and the fire can be approached similar to first floor fires.

The well developed, fully below grade fire in a building which has a life hazard or valuable contents, or which seriously exposes other buildings, presents a difficult problem and requires the expenditure of an effort commensurate with the objectives to be gained. The chief officer will evaluate the problems and develop strategy in accordance with his objectives.

## PROBLEMS OF DIFFICULT CELLAR FIRES

### LIFE HAZARD

As originally stated, the cellar fire presents a situation wherein the entire occupancy is exposed to heat and smoke from below. Occupants must make their exit down through conditions made perilous according to the degree of fire, the arrangement of vertical arteries, and other construction and fire protection features of the building.

### FIRE FIGHTING ACCESSIBILITY

As most cellar fires offer direct accessibility only from above, the heat barrier will frequently prevent an immediate advance of hose lines to the fire area.

In some cases, the single available stairway is inside the building, often beneath the building's main stairs. Other buildings have exterior cellar stairs or straight metal ladders beneath trap doors in sidewalks. In many cases, these outside entrances are chute delivery or sidewalk elevator enclosures.

Cellars of adjoining buildings may have connecting doors or have walls that can be breached with hand or power tools.

Cellars seldom have the ventilation features generally afforded above-ground areas. There is little need for natural light and air in an area generally reserved for storage of stock and service equipment. In addition to the openings provided for accessibility, there may be but a few scattered windows in the foundation. These are often heavily barred to discourage illegal entry or protected by sidewalk gratings to provide a continuous sidewalk alongside the building. The remaining means of ventilation are shafts, stairway openings and concealed arteries that provide openings to the upper floors and roof.

## STRATEGY AT CELLAR FIRE OPERATIONS

*LIFE HAZARD*

Where the building has stairs or other vertical arteries which permit smoke and heat to ascend to the occupied upper floors, the first hose line must be taken into the main hallway of the first floor, where it is generally positioned to protect the interior stairs. This tactic is consistent with the maxim that lines must be placed between endangered persons and the fire so that the endangered persons continue to have a means of egress. If emission of fire endangers the outside fire escape route, a line must also control this position. The interior line on the first floor can be used to check spread of fire via shafts, pipe recesses and hollow wall spaces.

Efficient ladder, rescue and squad companies will probably display their greatest versatility and initiative at a serious cellar fire in a non-fireproof building. These buildings are generally six or less stories in height and within the reach of the usual ladder equipment.

It may seem strange to the spectator to. see the immediate raising of an aerial to the roof when the fire is in the cellar. This action may accomplish more than any single act at a fire where the halls and vertical arteries are filled with smoke and accessibility to the roof is restricted to the use of such equipment. Opening all shafts at roof level will clear the halls and shafts, often permitting the occupants to use the stairs and allowing the engine company to enter the first floor area. It will also permit other fire fighters to ascend to the upper floors and join in the search, ventilation, and checking of shafts, recesses, partitions and other means of vertical fire extension. Particular attention should be given to the top floor and the rear of the building for these are the life danger points at a serious fire of this nature. When fully assured that all tenants have been evacuated and upper ventilation has been provided, the members can rejoin the other laddermen engaged in providing accessibility and ventilation for the actual cellar area.

### ACCESSIBILITY AND VENTILATION

At fires on the first or upper floors, ventilation is usually provided above or in front of the advancing hose lines. At cellar fires, limited accessibility and ventilation often force the fire fighter to struggle for openings and be less selective about their use. Whereas you would never open a roof skylight and direct a line down through the opening, it may be necessary to descend through a point of ventilation to attack a cellar fire. In the ideal situation where a number of cellar openings can be made, the lines should advance from one direction and drive the fire out through the points of ventilation at the opposite end. Seldom are such ideal patterns presented.

If it can be assumed that an efficient engine comany, or engine companies, entering a cellar can operate in a maximum of 100 hypothetical units of heat and smoke (units of discomfort), fires presenting more than 100 units will delay their effectiveness. Self-contained breathing equipment will permit easy entry when the units consist mainly of smoke with little heat, as at an oil burner fire, but for practical purposes, most fires consist of a related combination of smoke and heat. The more heat, the more smoke is a general rule. If 150 units are encountered after the usual points of accessibility and ventilation are provided, the problem becomes one of reducing the units to below 100 by increasing ventilation or adding accessibility for hose line use.

The coordination of accessibility and ventilation is crucial. If accessibility is provided with little increase in effective ventilation, the engine company members will be subjected to continued heat and smoke and will become exhausted or overcome before they can hit the fire source. If, on the other hand, ventilation is provided before hose line accessibility is increased, the fire will run away and soar beyond the 150 units described and will likely spread rapidly throughout the cellar and to the upper floors as well.

At fires which exceed the hypothetical 100 units, the chief develops the strategy for the attack by the subordinate officers. He must convey confidence to his subordinates despite the fact that he cannot predict success from any single action, but must plan at least one step ahead. His knowledge of tactical alternates gives him the understanding that one of the progressive plans will end in victory.

## CASES OF TACTICAL OPERATIONS AT CELLAR FIRES

The following cases describe the tactics of a chief in his struggle to use available alternates in controlling cellar fires.

## CASE 1 (Figure 1)

A stubborn fire is encountered in the cellar of an old residential building, four stories, non-fireproof brick and wood joist construction, 25 X 75 feet. The interior cellar stairway is directly beneath the main stairs and protected by a fire door on the first floor. There is an exterior entrance to the cellar at the front of the building and two small, below-grade windows at the rear of the cellar. On arrival, the heat conditions are severe, but the first floor is tenable. Apparatus response is three engine companies, two ladder companies and a rescue company.

1. *Primary Action*
The first hose line is taken into the main hall of the first floor to protect the interior stairs and be ready for use if the fire spreads via shafts, pipe recesses or hollow wall spaces. The door to the cellar is kept closed while the occupants are using the stairway.

The second hose line is immediately stretched to the cellar via the exterior cellar entrance by men with self-contained breathing apparatus. At this stage, this line is the primary attack line and should be advanced with a combination fog and solid stream nozzle.

Ladder units are deployed to perform tasks above the fire and in the cellar area. One group will ladder the building and remove occupants as required. These men will also ventilate all roof openings, search and ventilate upper floors and check for upward extension of fire. A second group will support the cellar attack by performing forcible entry, ventilation of rear cellar windows and first floor openings and removal of obstructions in the path of the advancing hose line.

## 2. *Supplementary Action*

The primary allocation of units has been made. The chief must now consider the possibility that control may not be achieved readily. He must plan his next move and consider his alternatives. A third engine and the rescue company remain at his disposal, but he cannot rush them into use before he has

Figure 1. *The first action at major cellar fires is to confine, and then extinguish.*

reevaluated the changing situation. If the fire has spread to the upper floors or if there is difficulty in evacuation of occupants, he must assign these units to support the activity at upper floor positions and secure additional help for further operations. Presuming the above-grade condition is favorable, he must now plan for more extensive cellar operations.

Concentration upon control of the cellar fire can now be directed toward providing added ventilation and further absorption of heat by successful hose line accessibility. The third line is placed to advance in unison with the second line from the outside stairs. The two lines will more than double the attack, for the heat will be reduced more rapidly and the presence of two adjacent attacking lines lends moral support to each hose crew and affords defensive protection on the flanks of each line.

To increase ventilation, the fire door protecting the interior cellar stairs may be opened and closed intermittently. The door is opened to allow heat and smoke to escape and closed to reduce any flame or severe heat spread to the upper floors. The rescue company can be positioned to cut a hole in the floor at the rear of the first floor close to windows to allow added area for the escape of the heat which will be pushed to the rear by the advancing cellar lines.

Since the area of the building is not excessive, these maneuvers will generally result in extinguishment of the fire. In unusual cases, the engine companies may fail to advance their hose lines and the fire will gain momentum. Additional help must be on hand at this point to effectuate further tactics and to replace exhausted companies.

The problem now becomes one of providing further heat reduction by unusual methods. These methods are considered unorthodox because they are of a hit or miss nature, uncertain in effect, and they generally require the withdrawal of attack lines.

The two attack lines in the cellar are partially withdrawn and an additional line is used through the rear cellar windows. The question will arise as to why this action was not taken earlier in preference to the use of two lines from the front stairway. The answer is that such window openings do not afford satisfactory accessibility for the advancement of the line. In addition, the windows are below grade and the angle of deflection will restrict the stream's coverage. Furthermore, the use of the line at this point will prevent the advance of any hose line from the opposite direction. However, at this stage of the fire, the use of the window line may cool down a portion of the rear of the cellar and then be shut down to allow the attack lines to press forward in a second attempt to extinguish the cellar fire.

At this stage, there are situations where breaching operations may be feasible. The breaching may be done from a partition within the building, from a street or yard, or through a wall from an adjoining cellar. In the latter case, it is well to consider what new hazard may be created. For example, if the adjoining building is an art gallery, the smoke may do irreparable damage, or if the occupancy is one of high hazard, the entrance of fire into another building may multiply the problems.

While these phases are operational, the chief must be preparing his next attack. Orders are issued to cut openings in the first floor to permit the insertion of cellar pipes or distributors. The cellar pipes will give greater reach, but some require manual operation. The distributor covers less area, but will operate unattended if the first floor becomes untenable. As soon as it becomes obvious that the attack lines cannot advance, the lines must be withdrawn and the cellar pipes and distributors inserted at points showing the greatest heat concentration on the first floor.

Heavy streams, including deck pipes or deluge sets, are now being placed at the first floor entrance to anticipate the use of the final alternative. If all else fails, the chief must resort to "flowing the floor," or flooding. This method is generally used when the first floor becomes unsafe or untenable. Flowing the floor requires the temporary use of a stream, or streams, directed at one spot or placed low to reduce first floor water damage. Its desired effect is to cover a porous floor with a few inches of water in the hope that the water will enter the cellar ceiling and cellar in a manner similar to an inefficient sprinkler system. In some cases, it has limited value because modern inexpensive floor coverings are often water resistant.

In the case of total flooding of most non-fireproof building cellars, the heavy lines are directed to cover the ceiling and all areas of the first floor, to cool stock and to flow into the cellar in such great volume as to partially fill the below-grade area with water. The principal disadvantages of its use are that it may hasten the collapse of the first floor or flow from the cellar into below-ground areas, such as subways or adjacent cellars. When areas are to be flooded, the chief must order a survey of adjacent areas to note where he may require the use of eductors to lessen the secondary damaging effects.

The chief will curtail operations at any stage along the way when success is achieved. But despite apparent success, he must be prepared for the next eventuality. He must be one step ahead of developments. It the advantage is lost at any stage, the fire will involve the upper floors and can no longer be considered a cellar operation.

## CASE 2 (Figure 2)

This fire has originated in the cellar of a two-story, 75 X 90-foot commercial building in a congested industrial section. The building is vacant except for storage in the cellar. The sprinkler system has been deactivated as part of a plan to modernize the building. In the rear, there is a narrow areaway leading to a below-ground entrance to the cellar. Two windows are below a sidewalk grating at the front of the building. The response is three engine companies, two ladder companies and a squad.

1. *Primary Action*
The first engine has stretched to the first floor and is examining for extension while the second engine stretches via the areaway stairway to the rear cellar and is entering the cellar. One ladder company is venting the upper floors and the roof while the other is supporting the cellar operation. The windows at the front of the cellar have been broken out by using a fire escape hook lowered through the slats of the sidewalk grating. A hole is being cut in the first floor flooring near the front windows to aid in ventilating the cellar. Members of the ladder companies are also assigned to move into the cellar area with the engine company. The squad has stretched a second line to move into the cellar from the rear. This action is justified since it is poor practice to use a single line in a cellar of moderate to large area where heavy fire is encountered.

Within a short time, the main body of fire in the cellar has been reduced, the ceiling is being opened, but a large volume of smoke continues to generate in the cellar and first floor, and there is evidence that the fire is running the partitions on the first floor.

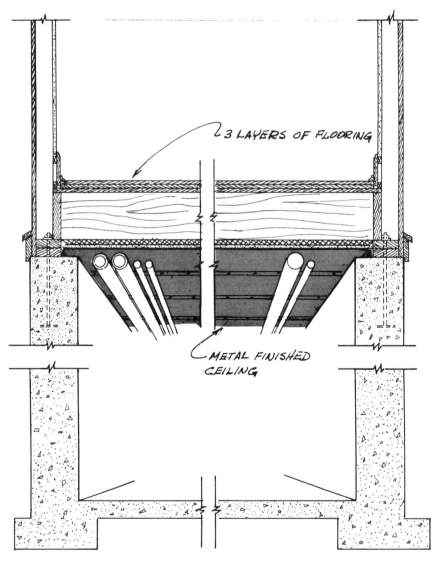

**Figure 2.** *If you cannot readily open cellar ceiling or cut flooring above, flow 1st floor to diminish fire intensity until ceiling and/or floor can be opened. If floor is not porous, triangular power saw cuts will permit entrance of water into ceiling space.*

## 2. *Evaluation and Supplementary Action*

Based on reports from subordinate officers and familiar signs of fire development, the chief realizes that heavy fire remains in the cellar ceiling bays. The pulling of the cellar ceiling is being retarded by the presence of the old sprinkler system and other piping, a metal ceiling, and a heavy smoke condition in the cellar. The presence of triple wood flooring is hampering the cutting of holes in the first floor.

The chief orders the third engine company to flow the first floor and moves another line to cover the second floor. The ladder unit working on the upper floors, pulls ceilings and opens partitions. The roof space is under observation and orders are issued to cut the roof if hot spots appear. A second alarm has been transmitted to fortify the assignment.

The lines in the cellar are withdrawn while the "flowing of the floor" proceeds for about two minutes. After the flow pipes are shut down, the cellar is reentered and another section of ceiling is pulled. The lines are again withdrawn and flow is renewed for a short period. This coordinated, alternate use of flow and cellar attack continues for about one hour, when the fire is placed under control. Minor extension to the upper floors was exposed and contained by the diligent openings made by ladder personnel and the use of streams by hand lines on the first and second floors.

## 3. *Critique*

It may well be asked why the chief resorted to flowing the floor in preference to other available procedures. The answer is to be found in the basic review of cellar fire fighting tactics. Directing a line through the front cellar windows or through a wall breach would accomplish less than the two lines which had extinguished the original cellar fire. The use of cellar pipes, distributors, or bent tip nozzles would be of limited use where the fire is raging in the ceiling bays and a triple flooring has to be opened for each nozzle or distributor insertion.

Flooding is unnecessary as the fire had not extended in volume to the first floor and water would not be required in depth in the cellar. The final key to selection of this method is based upon the fact that the flooring of the first floor is porous and water will flow rather evenly throughout the cellar ceiling bays. This permits control of the fire until such time as the ceiling can be opened and nozzles directed into each separate ceiling bay.

## CASE 3 (Figure 3)

This fire originated in the cellar of a commercial building, 50 X 90 feet, six stories high. The building is one of a group of several similar-type structures. The cellar and first floor are used for the manufacturing of plastics. The fire, a delayed discovery,

Figure 3. *Rigid control of personnel is essential for success at this fire. The unsupervised breaking of a window or opening of the roof will ruin the entire plan of action and result in a sudden eruption of fire.*

is reported just after midnight. Smoke is pushing out all windows on the upper floors. The first floor is untenable and it is evident that the cellar is completely involved in fire. A response of three engine companies and two ladder companies is present.

### 1. *Primary Action*

Upon arrival with the first units, the chief restrains the activity of all companies until he can properly survey the situation from all sides. Recognizing the potentialities, he summons additional help to cope with the obvious fire and exposure problems. He sends senior officers with walkie-talkies to the rear and to the adjacent buildings for surveys and immediate reports. He also begins to set up large caliber streams at the front of the fire building and places hand lines into the exposures. There is a reluctance to ventilate without careful consideration. Opening the roof or upper floors will create an upward draft and the full involvement of the building. Opening the first floor before upper level ventilation is provided will likely create a back draft.

Information relayed by subordinates confirms that the building is heavily involved with smoke at front and rear and that there are solid walls between the fire building and adjoining buildings. Fire is showing heavily at two rear cellar windows and two rear windows on the first floor. The watchman confirms that the building has no occupants at this time.

### 2. *Supplementary Action*

The primary strategy of the chief officer in this case is to refrain from accepting this fire as a cellar operation. Any of the standard cellar fire fighting procedures will probably result in a total spread of fire throughout the building.

Noting the severity of fire at four rear windows at lower levels, the chief decides to attempt an indirect attack. Four lines with large fog nozzles are stretched to the four rear windows and, at a given command, operated simultaneously into the heavy body of fire. While these lines are operating, the chief is hastily setting up large caliber streams at the front and rear of the building and moving his lines up to the roofs of the adjacent buildings.

The indirect method is unpredictable. Will the fog lines hit sufficient, lasting heat to generate steam capable of rising throughout the building? Will the vertical arteries permit the rise of steam in the same manner as they have previously allowed the rise of smoke? Will the roof and windows on the upper floors hold intact until the steam envelops the building? If these questions do not receive favorable answers, the fire will extend and the chief will order his large caliber streams into operation.

Where smoke was seen belching from the upper windows, steam now appears. The building is now opened and ventilated, and lines are advanced into the cellar and first floor. The remaining fire encountered is found within deep piles of materials in the cellar and on the first floor.

Later examination reveals that there had been a deep body of fire in the cellar, which burned through the flooring and extended to 25 percent of the first floor area. Heat stains are evident on the higher floors of the building.

3. *Critique*

What favorable or unfavorable features permitted the chief to use the indirect attack method at this fire?

In review, the factors are that no life hazard existed in the building; the building was heavily involved on arrival; ventilation would have caused drastic results; opening for the application of fog at low levels of high heat concentration were readily available; application of fog lines did not require any serious diversion of essential equipment. If the indirect method had failed, the four fog lines would have been moved into deluge sets to assist in control at the rear of the building.

The student is referred to Chapter 7—(The Indirect Method of Attack) for additional information on this type of strategy for extinguishment of fire.

## CASE 4

An isolated, vacant three-story brick and wood joist building on the outskirts of town is scheduled for demolition to make way for a road extension. Formerly used as a park department warehouse, the open floor areas are 60 X 80 feet. Upon arrival, the first units find the cellar fully involved with fire. Survey indicates that the cellar is accessible from the interior stairs, and there are no outside windows or entrances available.

1. *Primary Action*

The first units to arrive cannot enter the cellar and, therefore, commence to cut holes in the first floor for cellar pipes, distributors and ventilation. They also stretch lines for additional coverage.

2. *Supplementary Action*

On arrival, the chief surveys the situation and orders all units out of the building and lines directed from deluge sets into the first floor with intentions to flood the cellar.

Before the cellar fire is controlled by the flooding operation, there is evidence that fire is rising through partitions to the upper floors and roof. Lines are redirected upward, but, despite the large flow of streams, the building becomes totally involved, resulting in the collapse of the roof and one side wall.

3. *Critique*

At what stage did the chief make the decision that led to the loss of the structure?

The possible loss of the building was contemplated in the first strategic decision of the chief. He was obliged to arrange an "expenditure of an effort commensurate with the objective to be gained." Civilian life was not at stake, there were no exposures, and the building was scheduled for demolition. The sole objective in this case was to prevent injury to fire fighters. The fact that his total flooding effort failed is academic and without real consequence.

## CASE 5

Fire originates in the cellar of a five-story commercial non-fireproof building, 50 X 90 feet. Access to the cellar is through an inside open stairway at the center of the building, through an elevator hoistway at the sidewalk and through a small sidewalk delivery chute on a side courtyard. There are no windows at cellar level. No one is in the building.

The smoke and heat conditions are severe in the cellar and on the first floor, which is heavily loaded with stock. It is impossible to enter the first floor or cellar on arrival of the first units. Response is three engine companies, two ladder companies and a rescue company.

1. *Primary Action*

The first engine company places a powerful deck pipe stream in operation in front of the building and the water is directed along the ceiling of the first floor. The purpose of this line is to wet stock on the first floor, control the upward extension of fire and permit the excess water to flow the floor and enter the cellar.

The second engine company, finding that the sidewalk elevator hoist is at the bottom of the shaft, places a bent cellar pipe in operation in the hope that the stream will strike part of the parent body of fire in the cellar.

The third engine company sets up a similar bent cellar pipe operation through the chute delivery sidewalk opening on the courtyard.

The chief orders the ladder companies to refrain from ventilating. The rescue company is assigned to stretch a line to the cellar of the adjacent building, examine for fire extension and determine whether there are common openings between the cellar or suitable positions for a wall breach.

2. *Supplementary Action*

A second and third alarms are transmitted to afford coverage for exposure protection and exterior defensive operations.

The decision is made to refrain from ventilating, as the building is unoccupied. Upper-floor ventilation will not make the first floor tenable, and there is no indication of flame spread beyond the first floor. Furthermore, all voids through which fire could extend, as well as the upper floor areas themselves, are filled with smoke which is deficient in oxygen, since the inflow of air is proportional to the outflow of the products of combustion.

In addition to the coverage of exposures, the engine companies responding on the greater alarms set up to operate two hand lines through the front windows on the first floor and two more lines through the first floor rear windows.

As soon as heat conditions abate sufficiently on the first floor, the exterior lines to the first floor are shut down, the roof is now opened and efforts are made to enter the first floor to place distributors and additional cellar pipes in operation. Some stock is removed from the first floor to permit maneuverability.

The rescue company reports that minor fire has extended

through adjoining beam ends in the cellar of the adjacent building and that positions for direct cellar entry or breaching are impractical. They report that the ceiling is being opened along the course of the party wall and that they will be able to control fire extension with the one line at their disposal.

At this point, the chief has reached the crucial point of control. He must observe conditions, study the fire progress and decide what tactics are essential to his subsequent actions.

The first and most important decision involves the stability of the first floor. Is the floor sagging? Is there evidence of floor beams pulling out of the side walls? How much more of the first floor load can be readily removed? If stability is poor, he must resort to full cellar flooding. As stability is found favorable, he may move on to his choice of alternatives.

The decision is made at this point to shut down the bent cellar pipe operation and continue the use of the distributors accompanied by a single-line operation to continue flowing the first floor. In the interim, some ladder units are opening side walls and first floor ceilings to make certain that fire has not progressed beyond the first floor. The cellar pipes were shut down because they had probably hit all the fire within their range and further use would only fill the cellar with water. The distributors are in new positions and are likely to be striking sections not within reach of the bent cellar pipes. The flowing of the floor continues to control the fire in the cellar ceiling bays.

Observation at a later stage indicates that the fire continues to diminish in intensity. Further opening of a hole on the first floor reveals that the cellar ceiling is of the open joist type with no concealment. Based on this information, the flowing of the floor is discontinued and the distributors are repositioned to locations showing the greatest heat concentration. Another study of floor stability shows that the beams, though burned, are holding satisfactorily.

Positions formerly used for bent cellar pipes are now converted to water eduction points and the depth of water in the cellar is revealed to be about four feet. Further openings of the first floor are provided for ventilation of the cellar and eduction is increased at all possible points. As soon as the water level of the cellar drops to two feet, the cellar is cautiously entered and the remnants of the fire extinguished. Members operating in the cellar remain away from the area below the first floor stock until the merchandise is removed and the first floor load is lightened.

3. *Critique*

What features of strategy and tactics make this fire different from similar fires previously described?

The major difference of this fire is the extensive use of various alternative tactics by the chief in charge. Assuming command after the fire had involved the cellar and had restricted first floor operations, he combined almost all tactical operations to isolate and finally control the fire. It is in his coordination of efforts that his skill is manifest.

The chief must not only know the tactical moves to make and their normal sequence, but he also must understand the reason for each move so that he can combine practical operation with theory.

The indirect method of attack would not have been suited for this fire because the major heat locations were not directly accessible in the early stages of the fire.

## CASE 6

A group of three one-story stores, each 30 x 110 feet, are undergoing alterations. Two of the three stores are combined to form a supermarket 60 x 110 feet in area. An opening was cut through a cellar wall near the front of the building to permit the common use of the two cellars by the supermarket occupant. A fire originates in the front of the supermarket. There is an interior cellar stairway at the rear of the first floor and two sidewalk trap doors at the front of the building.

1. *Primary Action*

On arrival, the district chief discovers little smoke on the first floor but evidence of heavy localized fire in the cellar. The first engine company stretches a line through the supermarket and descends the interior cellar stairs at the rear. A ladder company opens the front sidewalk trap doors and heavy smoke is ventilated from the one with a built-in delivery chute. The second shows much less smoke and has a straight ladder for descent to the cellar.

Moving down the rear stairs, the first engine company advances below the heat level, but it encounters difficulty in moving the charged line and finding the opening into the other side of the cellar. The second engine company assists them on the line and, after donning self-contained breathing equipment, moves up to advance the first line. The third engine company stretches to the outside entrance and is ready to descend the straight ladder. The chief, reluctant to have a line working directly against the advance of the first line, holds this line at the outside position.

A ladder company, assigned to cut a hole in the first floor near the front of the supermarket, reports that the floor appears to be constructed of two inches of concrete. Malls and a pneumatic drill are placed in operation to assist in opening the floor.

The officer advancing the first line reports that he has not contacted the main body of fire and has encountered a labyrinthine layout in the cellar with heat intensity increasing. After a period of time, the chief, disappointed with the advancement of the line and fearful for the safety of the men, orders this line withdrawn to cover the first floor and orders the advance of the second line from the front outside entrance.

*2. Supplementary Action*
On arrival, the division chief receives a report of conditions from the district chief and notes that the second line has been hurriedly brought out of the cellar after encountering a severe heat buildup.

The division chief summons additional help and concerns himself with regrouping his forces and developing further strategy to cope with the increasing problems.

While a fire-resistive floor will help contain a fire in a cellar, such floors do retard fire fighting operations and do prevent effective flowing of the floor. The division chief orders a bent cellar pipe directed into the cellar through the sidewalk chute opening and another line into the adjacent store cellar to check for extension of fire and to search for a breaching position. Distributors and cellar pipes are set up for use through the concrete floor and the first floor is ventilated fully to relieve smoke that will accumulate in the store after the floor is opened.

The roof is being opened and sidewalls are being examined for extension.

At about the same time as a few floor openings are made, a company officer reports that the concrete floor does not extend beyond the side wall vegetable bins and that the fire has developed behind the false, porcelain type, side wall panels. The fire has now entered the roof space and the officer in charge of the line in the adjacent cellar reports fire in the ceiling.

As lines and ladder companies are being directed to the extension points, the owner of the supermarket arrives on the scene. The division chief questions the owner about the construction of the cellar beams and is informed that the concrete floor is supported by new, unprotected, steel beams set to support the additional weight of the concrete floor.

Realizing that the fire is diminishing the strength of the cellar structural supports, the chief orders all personnel out of the supermarket and sets up defensive operations. In a short time, sections of the first floor collapse and the building becomes involved to the point of almost total destruction.

3. *Critique*

What lessons can be learned from the failures at this type of operations?

Perhaps, the most vital lesson learned is the importance of a swift and effective direct attack at the early stages of a fire of this type. First evidence indicated that the fire was localized toward the front and one side of the cellar. This was shown by the contrast in heat and smoke showing upon ventilation of the sidewalk openings. Furthermore, it was poor tactics to place confidence in a hose line that had to be stretched 110 feet to the rear of the store, turned directly about and then advanced almost an equal distance toward the front. Any hope of early control of this fire would be found in an early descent through the straight ladder at the outside entrance. The cross-over was near the front and the fire was localized a short distance from this opening.

In defense of the first-arriving chief, you might say he is a victim of the Monday morning quarterbacks. He might not, on arrival, know the layout of the cellars. Furthermore, if the cellar was not partitioned, he might have, ideally, entered the cellar from the rear and driven the fire successfully out through the ventilation points at the front of the structure.

Accepting this hypothesis, his failure remains in the fact that he stayed with the first line too long. There was evidence of lack of movement and valuable time was lost at this crucial period.

The second major lesson is that a fire-resistive first floor in an otherwise combustible building can often be more of a hindrance than a help at a serious cellar fire.

## CASE 7

A fire has been burning, undiscovered, in the cellar of a 38-story, 200 x 200-foot, fireproof office building in the busy financial section of town. The first units arriving at dawn encounter severe heat near the cellar entrance at the base of the interior main stairway. Contact with the service manager, who opened the building a few moments before the department's arrival, reveals that this portion of the cellar, about 50 x 200 feet, is used for general storage and includes office furniture, office records, electrical equipment including reels of wire, showcase equipment and a varied assortment of building maintenance material. The room is generally rectangular except for a short L-shape at the end of the room. There are three 1 x 3-foot windows in the wall at the end of the L but no other openings in the room. The remaining portions of the cellar are used as a cafeteria and service area and have few window openings as the area is air-conditioned.

1. *Primary Action*
The first engine company enters the cellar with self-contained breathing apparatus and deflects a solid stream against the ceiling with the hope of establishing a foothold at the entrance to the fire area. While a second line is being stretched to back them up, the ladder company opens the three small windows at the end of the storage area. The first engine company switches to fog and finds instant relief. Encouraged by this maneuver, they push forward and advance about 40 feet along the center aisle of the room.

The second line arrives in position none too soon. They have all they can do to protect the men from the first line as they scramble back to the door with burns of the exposed skin of their necks and ears. The third engine company, also equipped with masks, assists the injured members to the street and then is able to pull back the first line and place it in operation alongside the second line at the entrance to the storage room.

The chief consults with the service manager and gathers information relative to the building features. Based on the knowledge received, he succeeds in accomplishing the shutdown of the air conditioning system and its intakes. Vertical ventilation is discouraged as it will result in smoke stratification at intermediate floors and the lower offices will be filled with smoke and heat.

*2. Supplementary Action*

Inspection of the first floor and upper regions of the building reveals that the fire and smoke are being confined to the cellar and that all fireproof features of the building are intact.

At this stage, the chief summons additional help and special-calls the mask service unit to the scene. This unit will supply additional mask equipment and will refill expended air cylinders.

Anticipating a prolonged operation, the chief decides to organize each line action into three separate rotating company units. The first to operate the line, the second to stand in ready reserve, the third to replenish their air supply and gain moments of relief in the fresh air. Each unit officer gives his unit roster slip to the safety officer, who checks the presence of all members of each unit as they come out of the cellar.

When available help arrives, three units are assigned to the operation of a third line in the cellar. Two of the lines now operating with fog nozzles are placed at the side aisle and advance slowly, driving the heat and smoke ahead of them. The third line, operating at the center aisle, directs a sweeping solid stream to kill fire in advance of the reach of the fog lines.

The progress is slow and it is found that when all three lines are operated at full capacity, the steam and heat buildup increases the discomfort of the members. Optimum advancement is attained when the solid stream is operated only at intermittent periods.

The units continue in their systematic relief for one hour, after which time the fire has diminished to the point of control.

*3. Critique*

Where ventilation and access to a fireproof cellar are adequate, these fires, although hot, are readily controlled. Where the fire is large and ventilation is inadequate, fire fighting becomes a problem of fortitude and perserverance. The heat buildup becomes so great that the firemen feel as though they are operating in a furnace.

Safety features, as developed at this fire, are vital as members may exhaust their air supply and become lost in the maze of underground passageways. Members must stay close to the hose line, which is their guide line to a safe exit.

The case of the men on the first line is an example of a hazard encountered in using fog nozzles without reasonable ventilation. This company found comfort while driving the fire ahead of them. As the windows could not take off the smoke, steam and heat being driven forward, the excesses gathered along the side areas and were suddenly drawn into the rear of the fog nozzle, much in the manner of an exhaust fan. Pulled into this area, it passed the backs of the men operating the line and burned them severely on the exposed portions of their necks and ears.

## CONCLUSIONS

Moderate to large cellars in non-fireproof buildings should be inspected thoroughly with a view to recommending the installation of automatic sprinkler systems. If the ventilation, accessibility and fire loading problems could create difficult fires such as the one just described, sprinklers are the outstanding method of control. A non-automatic sprinkler may be useful provided the installation includes a thermostatic alarm to assure prompt discovery and reporting of the fire. When delay in discovery occurs, the pipes may be subjected to structural failure before the fire department arrives to pump water into the system. Old perforated-pipe systems are not reliable, for age weakens the supports and corrosion partially closes the water orifices.

Cellars of fireproof buildings should be surveyed to correct difficult storage conditions. Generally the conditions can be alleviated by proper subdivision or provisions for adequate ventilation and accessibility. Where the design of a large cellar area will not allow improvements of this nature, a sprinkler system should be recommended.

# Chapter 15

# High-Expansion Foam

High-Expansion Foam has emerged within the last 10 years as an acceptable and efficient method for assisting the fire chief in coping with certain difficult fires. The manufacturers have researched, tested and refined their high-expansion foam equipment, and today there are many fire departments throughout the country using this relatively new medium of fire control.

As early as 1961, Factory Mutual Research Corporation tested generating equipment in 12,000 and 50,000 cfm units and reported it to be a practical method of fire protection for special applications that are otherwise difficult to protect. They said that foam generators can fill an entire building in minutes, that the foam is a good heat insulator and that it is effective on ordinary combustible surface fires, as well as flammable liquids.

Water in the form of either spray or solid stream is the primary extinguishing agent in every fire department. It is the cheapest and most effective for most fires. But where water cannot reach the base of a fire, such as in cellars and sub-cellars, mine shafts, sewers, and other places generally inaccessible for stream pentration, high-expansion foam has, in some of these instances, proven its worth.

Paradoxically, as it may appear, water is the chief extinguishing agent of high-expansion foam. It is rather unfortunate that it is classified as a foam, for most fire fighters recognize foam as a smothering agent, since the chief attribute of chemical and mechanical foams are their capacities to flow on a liquid surface and to exclude air from the burning vapors.

High-expansion foam has similarities, but also features that are quite distinct from its counterparts. While cooling is only an incidental feature of chemical and mechanical foams, it is an important characteristic of high-expansion foam. In fact, its efficiency is correlated to the amount of water within the foam that reaches the fire area. According to the textbooks, it controls fire by:

1. Cooling
2. Smothering
3. Reducing the oxygen content by steam dilution of atmosphere. However, it has other qualities, and these can be learned only by reviewing the experiences of fire departments in actual fire situations.

## BASEMENT FIRE [1]

The four-story building was of brick-timber construction, 100 X 150 feet. The basement was 8000 square feet, divided by a masonry wall running from front to back and pierced by a single door near the rear. For all intents and purposes, it could be considered one area, since the door was open. There were three window openings on the rear alley and a rear exterior basement door.

### FIRE ORIGIN

The fire started among office supplies stored in the southwest corner of the basement. Heavy smoke was in the basement and spreading throughout the upper floors. The fire was spreading rapidly throughout the basement.

---

(1) This fire was reported in Fire Engineering, Jan. 1971, by staff correspondent R. L. Nailen.

An offensive attack was initiated, but the heat barrier and inadequate venting facilities made it impossible for the men to endure the atmosphere, necessitating a change in strategy.

### HIGH-EXPANSION FOAM APPLICATION

A three-foot-square hole was cut in the first floor near the sidewalk and foam application was started. Non-vital openings through which foam might escape were closed or blocked up. Once the quality of foam was properly adjusted, the entire 72,000 cubic feet of basement space was filled in about 55 minutes. The fire was out except for smoldering pockets remaining in the ceiling. The smoke was gone. A spray nozzle was used to clear a path through the foam to examine the basement.

The type foam used in this situation had an expansion rate of 100 to 1. Theoretically, enough foam was used to fill the basement area twice. Heat and water in the basement apparently broke down a considerable portion of the foam.

### LESSONS LEARNED

1. This fire was fought effectively and efficiently with high-expansion foam.
2. The foam controlled the fire and displaced the smoke so that later entry by firemen was made without discomfort.
3. The fire fighters tended to become disoriented while moving through the foam and, therefore, procedures were established to keep an accurate record of whereabouts of personnel. Also, men were assigned to work in teams.
4. This type high-expansion foam remained thick even after five hours.

## BASEMENT FIRE [2]

A basement was 75 X 100 feet with a 12-foot ceiling. The

---

(2) Fire Engineering, Feb. 1965, p. 39.

building was an old flour mill, weakened in some areas because of the fire, with collapse possibilities.

Unnecessary ventiliation was blocked off and two high-expansion foam units were activated. It is reported that within a relatively short time, the entire basement was flooded with foam, which immediately controlled the fire.

*LESSONS LEARNED*

1. Where access and ventilation are limited and first-floor structural failure is a possibility, high-expansion foam should receive serious consideration as the means of controlling the fire.
2. In this situation, an orginal attempt was made to get a cellar pipe in operation from the first floor. But the intensity of the heat at the first-floor level prevented the accomplishment of this task. Flooding the cellar with foam enabled fire fighters to work effectively above the fire.
3. "One of the outstanding characteristics of high-expansion foam is that a small amount of water containing a little foam concentrate can make a lot of foam. But the fire-killing capability of the foam is no greater than the same amount of water applied to the fire with equal efficiency. Thus it must be appreciated that there is a relationship between the size of the fire and the size of the foam generator that can control the fire." [3] In this fire, by using two high-expansion foam units simultaneously, the rate of application was doubled. This considerably improved the chances of success. The longer the fire burns, the greater the dissipation of the foam by heat. If small foam generators are used in large-area fires, the foam will be as ineffective as a 1½-inch line on a large fire in a lumberyard.

## GOLD MINE FIRE [4]

Approximately one million gallons of high-expansion foam was

---

(3) Jamison, Will B.—"High-Expansion Foam in the Fire Dept."—Fire Journal, Nov. 1967, p. 46.

(4) Dektar, Cliff—"High-Expansion Foam Controls Abandoned Mine Fire"—Fire34.

used in an abandoned gold mine. The shaft was filled at times and foam flowed out another shaft 100 feet away and 50 feet lower. Two hours after the operation stopped, the foam had dissipated and a small amount of smoke was coming from the shaft. Inspection revaled that the fire was completely out except for a small amount of smoldering material.

*LESSONS LEARNED*

1. Within 10 minutes after starting foam application, large volumes of steam were emitted from the shaft. The steam generation continued for a long period of time and until about 30 minutes before the foam generator was shut down. The foam was completely dissipated two hours after discontinuance of the operation. This indicates that the effectiveness of this foam lies primarily in its capacity to act as a carrier of water to the seat of the fire, where the water is then converted to steam. By going through this process of vaporization, the water's cooling effects are maximized. Furthermore, the steam will dilute the oxygen, diminishing or smothering the fire.

## GASOLINE TANK TRAILER [5] (Figure 1)

A locomotive hit a gasoline tank trailer erupting in a massive gasoline fire along the tracks. The trailer separated from the tractor, and overturned.

Six 1¹/₂-inch lines with fog applicators were used to control convection and radiant heat. High-expansion foam with an expansion rate of 1000 to 1 covered the liquid surface in 2¹/₂ minutes and controlled the fire. In this situation, the foam was delivered through a 3¹/₂ to 4-foot diameter canvas tube, coupled in sections for a 300-foot length.

---

(5) Dektar, Cliff—"High-Expansion Foam Passes Los Angeles Test"—Fire Engineering, May 1964.

1. Gasoline tank vehicle fires plague the fire fighting force. They frequently occur on highways where water supply is very limited. High-expansion foam with its fabulous expansion rate can quickly cover the spill, and there is generally adequate water in the booster tank of fire vehicles to supply the water demands. Speed of coverage at time of arrival is the key factor, for it controls the vast heat output, improving rescue opportunities and diminishing exposure problems. Once the spill has been blanketed, it is advisable to adjust the generator to decrease the expansion rate and thereby thicken the foam blanket. There are foam generators presently on the market which permit the fireman operator to adjust the air rate and the liquid rate separately, permitting a degree of control over the thickness of the blanket.

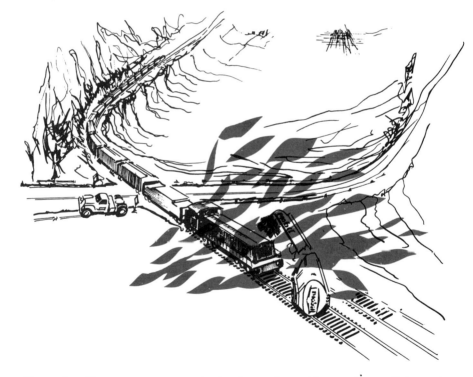

Figure 1. *Almost every community has been plagued by gasoline spill fires. A sufficient rate of application of high expansion foam will control most of these fires in minutes.*

2. Wind can be an important factor at these fires. Operations should be initiated on the windward side to prevent the products of combustion or high temperatures from interfering with foam production. The wind will accelerate the foam movement across a liquid surface. On the other hand, if a foam blanket has little density, the wind can readily cause its dissipation. Under unfavorable wind conditions, the expansion rate should be reduced to thicken the blanket. If the day is extremely gusty, or if high winds prevail, it may be necessary to resort to mechanical foam.

3. In this situation, a foam generator was situated 300 feet from the fire. This is a distinct advantage since the products of combustion and the temperature of the fire can substantially interfere with the volume and stability of foam production. A temperature of 150°F at the inlet fan will drain 90 percent of the water within a two-minute period. Most of the water will drop out and never reach the fire.[6] At the current state of the art, high expansion foam is not a reliable fire-extinguishing agent when air from within the hazard area is used for foam generation.

4. The rate of application is of extreme importance in all fire situations. However, it has greater significance for a gasoline fire or other flammable liquids with low flash points. Time is the critical factor, since the liquid readily vaporizes, and the fire reaches greater proportions in shorter periods of time than class A fires. The greater the heat intensity, the greater the dissipation rate of the foam. Therefore, it is advisable to be equipped with the large capacity foam trucks or to use a number of portable units simultaneously. In addition, in a building fire, steam will be contained for longer periods than in outdoor fires. This adds to the foam generating problems in outdoor situations.

5. There have been at least three street or highway accidents involving tank vehicles where high expansion foam was used with success. Many tests and demonstrations have shown the capability of high expansion foam to control and extinguish

---

(6) Williams, John R.—"Effects of Combustion Products on High-Expansion Foam"—Fire Journal, Nov. 1968.

class B fires. In tests at UL and FM, high-expansion foam has extinguished all the standard test fires. A high expansion foam truck rated at 13,500 cfm has extinguished demonstration fires involving 10,000 square feet of gasoline and 15,000 square feet of oil.[7]

The United States Naval Applied Science Laboratory has been studying foams with expansion ratios up to 500 to 1. The investigation showed that the advantage of high expansion foam was its fluidity and ability to roll over itself, resulting in quicker coverage and more rapid extinction of fire. The less viscous foams are the most effective in extinguishing large-area fires because of their rapid coverage, despite the fact that these foams lose their water rapidly and disintegrate faster than the more viscous foams.[8]

Research, test demonstrations, and three actual fire experiences will not unfold the complete picture of high expansion foam on gasoline tank vehicle fires. At the fire scene, solid and heavy fog streams must be used in certain situations to cool the gasoline tank, to reduce internal pressures, and to reduce the velocity of escaping vapors. Heavy fog streams are used to dilute the gasoline vapor zone and to channel the flow of the explosive vapor. What will be the deleterious effects of these water streams on the development of the foam blanket? Can the fire force develop procedures whereby the water streams and high expansion foam will complement each other?

6. We are indeed fortunate to have this new medium for fire control of gasoline vehicles on highways. As with all new tools, experience with all of the variable factors learned from a multiplicity of fires will dictate how, where and when to use the equipment for effective fire control.

---

(7) Jamison, Will B.—"High-Expansion Foam in the Fire Dept."—Fire Journal, Nov. 1967.

(8) Lambert, Milton—"Using High-Expansion Foam on Hydrocarbon Fires"—Fire Engineering, Apr. 1965.

**LUMBERYARD FIRE** [9]

A lumberyard was 2000 feet long and 1000 feet deep. The atmospheric temperature was 55°F, and originally the breeze was from the south and light. But typical of lumber yard fires, the wind velocity increased to 14 mph and shifted to the southwest.

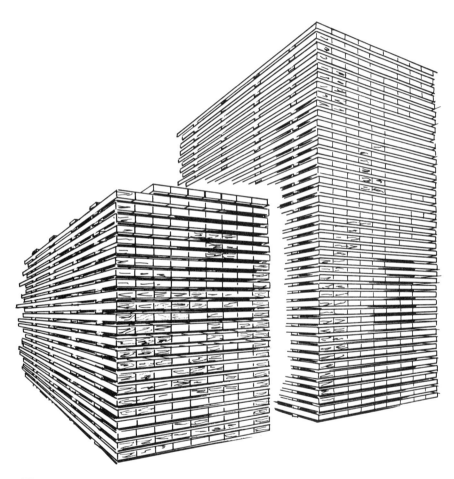

Figure 2.   *The mode of stacking lumber in yards promotes quick burning since air is present throughout every layer of the pile.*

(9) O'Brien, Donald M.—"Foam Controls Lumber Yard Fire"—Fire Engineering, July 1965.

The fire started in about the center of the yard and before the arrival of fire department units, the sawdust collection house had been consumed and 10 to 15 large piles of lumber were burning furiously. It is estimated that one-fifth of the yard was involved in fire.

*FEATURES OF LUMBERYARDS*

Before considering the application of high expansion foam to this particular fire situation, let us review some of the factors involved in lumberyard fires, and the experiences of fire departments in coping with these disasters.

A chief arriving at a lumberyard situation where the areas are large has great apprehension because of the potentiality of losing the entire yard to fire. If the locality features similar hazardous occupancies, he is faced with a possible conflagration.

The lumber piles vary in height from 12 to 20 feet. Horizontal spaces are used between layers of boards to increase air circulation to assist in seasoning the lumber. The fire gets into these spaces, which are out of reach of major streams operating at distances. (Figure 2)

The irregular lengths of lumber comprising a pile present additional air spaces at each end of the pile, which adjoins other piles having similar uneven ends. Fire communicates quickly from one pile to another through these spaces. Remote streams cannot fully cope with this type of fire extension.

In addition, it is common to have many frame buildings within a yard, such as storage sheds for seasoned and finished lumber, shops for making window frames, doors, interior trim, etc., carpentry and planing shops, and even paint storage sheds. Convection currents and radiant heat will seriously expose these buildings.

Fire in lumberyards will give off dense volumes of smoke, particularly when the lumber is partially green. This smoke is very irritating to the eyes and respiratory organs of firemen.

After gaining some headway, the fire develops great heat and volumes of sparks and brands which, when carried by the wind, can extend the fire for a considerable distance. The updraft or velocity of rising heat may carry blocks of burning wood hundreds of feet. These burning brands have sufficient weight at times to break through skylights on roofs of buildings and fall through and start fires inside buildings.

### OFFENSIVE ATTACK

Where two, three or four piles are involved on arrival, a direct offensive attack is feasible to control and extinguish the fire. Hand lines should be stretched and operated in through lumber piles, and between spaces to stop extension of the fire throughout the piles. Hose lines with distributors attached can be used between piles where their uneven ends are arranged back to back. (Figure 3) This can best be done by fastening the distributor hose to a ladder laid on top of two adjoining piles to bridge the uneven ends of the piles. Deck pipes and other major stream appliances can be used to wet down nearby piles, to spray tops of burning piles, to break up heat and to extinguish sparks and brands.

### DEFENSIVE ATTACK

Where 10 to 15 large piles of lumber were involved, fire departments have always been on the defensive. Since lumber-yard areas are so extensive, deck pipe and ladder pipe streams have inadequate reach to cover other than the perimeter of the fire. The convection heat generally negates positioning of apparatus on the leeward side of the fire. The fire, therefore, burns within the piles and from one end to the other end of the uneven piles. This represents failure.

### HIGH-EXPANSION FOAM (Figure 4)

In a fire where 10 to 15 piles were involved, a foam generator was placed in operation and a 6 to 10-foot foam blanket controlled the fire in the lower portions of the stacked lumber.

Figure 3. *These distributors act like large sprinkler heads. They are positioned at locations where fire spread is greatest and where fire is inaccessible.*

The fire fighters then brought hand lines through the foam and knocked out fire in the tops of the piles. It was estimated that 1.5 million gallons of foam were generated, using about 1500 gallons of water. The foam was applied in approximately 30 minutes. The fire was controlled and confined within this time, and the major portion of the yard, including trucks and sheds, was saved.

1. The Perth Amboy, N.J., Fire Department, which extinguished this fire, displayed great ingenuity and versatility. Imagination and resourcefulness conquered a heretofore unconquerable fire situation. The department added a new dimension to fire tactics, and that is, where heat is the barrier to offensive movements in lumberyards and similar situations, use high expansion foam as a heat shield to protect advancing firemen.

2. Walking through foam is a new experience to firemen. Their

Figure 4. *The high expansion foam provides a heat shield, permitting firemen to advance a hand line. As a safety measure, firemen should stay with the line and remain close together. If heat becomes excessive, the men can duck into the foam blanket for protection.*

movement through the blanket will cause some of the bubbles to burst, and sufficient oxygen will be released to allow the men to breathe normally. When the blanket is not above their heads, at times they will find it more comfortable to duck within the cool, non-toxic foam than to expose themselves to heat and smoke.

3. When working in high or extensive blankets or within structures flooded with foam, they can readily become disoriented and experience a swimming sensation, perhaps somewhat like weightlessness. Safety precautions are necessary to prevent injury or loss of personnel.

*HIGH-EXPANSION FOAM* [10]

The Greensburg, Pa., Volunteer Fire Department responded with a foam truck to a department store fire. They were on a mutual aid assignment. The local fire department had responded to this nighttime fire, which had originated in a merchandise storage area. But they soon realized, by using the usual fire fighting methods, that they would not be able to stop the fire from involving the entire store. High expansion foam was then pumped into the building and the fire was contained within the storage area. Some extent of the fire is revealed by the fact that the property loss was estimated at a quarter of a million dollars. But the high expansion foam prevented the loss of the entire $5 million structure.

Greensburg responded with the same foam unit to a one-story restaurant fire which was threatening buildings along an entire block. The fire had vented itself through the roof and had jumped to the roof of an adjoining hardware store. The fire had been burning for 30 minutes before their arrival. The firemen filled the restaurant building entirely with foam and let the foam build up to a thickness of 4 ft. above the roof. Within 10 minutes, the foam had snuffed out the fire.

### CONCLUSIONS

1. The one-story restaurant and the one-story department store

---

(10) "Have High-Expansion Foam Truck. Will Travel."—Fire Engineering, Oct. 1968

have similarities to taxpayers and supermarkets in some of their structural features and occupancy hazards.

2. When the fire fighting forces are on the defensive and are pouring tons of water into these occupancies, the water damage is vast.

3. Fire fighting forces can continue to fight these fires throughout the entire night, thereby depleting availability of apparatus and manpower for the rest of the area.

4. The Greensburg Fire Department demonstrated in two instances the capability of high expansion foam to fill a cavity and control a class A fire in a relatively short period of time. However, they used a foam generator capable of producing 13,500 cubic feet per minute, while most fire departments are using generators of much less capacity. It appears that the larger capacity generators, which are used on fires in large-area structures such as taxpayers and supermarkets, will assist fire departments in moving from a defensive to an offensive strategy, controlling the fire much faster and considerably reducing the fire loss.

5. In industry, fire protection systems have been developed which generate as much as 660,000 cubic feet of high expansion foam per minute, and systems of 150,000, 90,000, and 54,000 cfm are fairly common in industry today. They are designed to fill the building cavity within seven minutes and have the generating capacity to fill the structure three times.

6. At major fires in New York City, it was customary to use streams with a flow of approximately 1000 gpm and a range of 100 feet. Now, the heavy artillery consists of streams with a delivery of 3500 gpm or more with a range of over 300 feet. Since the inception of these new super-streams, fires are being brought under control much more quickly, and the need for fourth, fifth and greater alarms has been substantially reduced. I believe a parallel exists between the discharge capacities of streams and high expansion foam generators.

## 5 & 10 VARIETY STORE FIRE

The building has dimensions of 90 X 100 feet with a ceiling height of ten feet. There is an open interior stairway located on

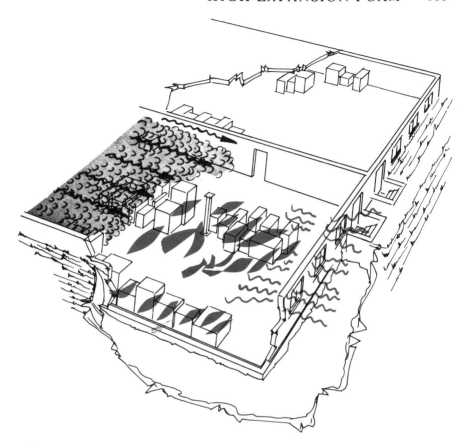

Figure 5. *The advancing foam blanket has some of the characteristics of a large fog stream, in that it pushes heat, smoke and fire ahead of it. Therefore, it is essential to provide rearward ventilation.*

the west wall of the building about 20 feet from the front, connecting the cellar with the first floor. There are windows at the cellar level in the rear of the building. The only other opening to the cellar is a chute located in the front of the building.

### FIRE DEVELOPMENT

Flame was blowing out of the rear windows of the cellar. Fire has extended via the open stairs to the first floor. The fire forces readily extinguished the fire on the first floor, and two lines were used in the rear to darken fire in this area. The heat barrier prevented access to the cellar, and fire continued to burn vigorously.

### HIGH EXPANSION FOAM (Figure 5)

At this stage, the high expansion foam generator was placed into operation and the foam was delivered into the cellar area through the chute located in the front of the building.

### QUESTIONS

*1. Why is it so important to vent the rear of the building at the cellar level while filling the cavity with foam from the front of the building?*

*2. When would conditions on the first floor change from hot and smoky to normal because of foam application?*

3. *The cubic dimensions of the cellar are 100' X 90' X 10' or 90,000 cubic feet. What size foam generator would be appropriate for this situation?*

4. *During operations, the wind changes causing the products of combustion to engulf the foam generator. What effect would this have on foam production?*

5. *As the foam blanket moves rearward, the fire will become more intense in the rear portion of the cellar, and flames will belch through the rear windows. Since heat intensity accelerates foam dissipation, is it advisable to use rear exterior streams to cool this fire?*

6. *How can the progress of the foam blanket be ascertained?*

7. *Presume there is a large hanging ceiling, accommodating utility pipes, electrical lines, etc., all wrapped with combustible insulation. What action?*

8. *The floor openings indicate a stoppage in the movement of the foam blanket. About 70% of the fire has been extinguished. The open stairway is filled with foam.*

*Two teams consisting of an officer and two firefighters each are ordered to proceed down the foam-filled stairway with hose lines.*

*What safety procedures would be appropriate for this evolution?*

1. As the mountain of foam flows rearward, the air is compressed, increasing the supply of oxygen to the remaining fire with a concomitant increase in temperature and intensity of fire. These factors would interfere substantially with foam efficiency.

   If the air was compressed in the rear, and there was no ventilation, this would hinder or perhaps prevent the movement of the foam blanket to the rear area.

2. This is one of the chief advantages of high expansion foam. As the blanket moves toward the rear, and especially after it passes the open stairs, it will clear the first floor of smoke, reduce temperatures, and ease the problem for the firefighters performing their duties above the fire.

3. A 13,500 cubic feet generator. This has a capacity of filling the cellar in about 7 minutes. This approximates the standard established for industrial fire protection. Of course, the cellar is fire loaded and theoretically this would reduce the needed quantity of foam. However, the heat of the fire will dissipate some of the foam. We do not have computers at fires, so a rule of thumb should be established, the same as used in our hydraulic calculations for water. Theoretically we apply more water than needed; the same concept should apply to foam.

   If portable generators of 5000 cubic foot capacity are available, three of them should be used simultaneously. An inadequate rate of application has led to many failures of foam application at fires, with the result that the value of high expansion foam is questioned. However, the measure of foam efficiency should be correlated with its rate of application. Ten 1½-inch fog lines, if used all the hours of the day, would not have any effect on a major lumberyard fire. This is not because water has failed in its function, but rather that the rate of application is totally inadequate for a massive fire. Provide enough water, and adequate range of streams, and the fire will be conquered.

The New York City Fire Department has recently introduced four satellite units with nozzle capacities of 1300 to 4700 gpm and a range of 300 to 400 feet. With this type of artillery, major lumberyard fires are quickly brought under control. Similarly, provide adequate high expansion foam generating equipment at those fires where the use of foam is feasible, and then we will have a proper standard to measure the worthiness of this type foam.

4. Elevated temperatures at the inlet fan will drain water from the foam solution. Since the effectiveness of foam is related to the amount of water which reaches the fire, elevated temperatures will have a considerable adverse effect on the foam solution. In addition, the high expansion foam is not a reliable extinguishing agent when contaminated with smoke. There is no choice. The generator would have to be moved to an atmosphere free of smoke and heat.

5. No. If the foam movement is progressing, it is improvident to use these exterior streams. The force of the streams will drive heat and smoke into the foam blanket, breaking it down.

   It is advantageous to keep flame, heat and smoke expelling from the rear windows. Do not change their direction of flow with exterior stream application.

   At the time of arrival of fire forces, and before the application of high expansion foam, employ the exterior streams to reduce heat intensity, but not thereafter.

6. When steam emerges from the rear windows, the atmosphere above the fire returns to normal and the foam flows up the inside open stairs, indications of foam effectiveness are evident.

   However, it is expedient to make openings in the first floor at about 20 feet intervals from front to rear of building. Heat accumulates at the ceiling level, and high temperatures will prevent total flooding. The holes in the floor will release heat and allow foam to escape through the openings and indicate the rate of progress of the foam movement. The diameter of these openings should be adequate to accommodate a distributor. This will provide an alternative to fire attack in case of failure of foam application.

Furthermore, with these openings the firefighters can make a determination of the presence of a concealed ceiling space.

7. Floor openings would have to be made adequate in size, so that some of the ceiling could be pushed down providing a channel for foam penetration.

8. A. Firemen should work in small teams with the officer in charge of the team moving with the men and maintaining close liaison with each man.

   B. Hose or safety lines should be provided for each team as a guide for quick egress.

   C. The men should crawl through the foam blanket, and the first man should use a six-foot hook, pike pole or similar tool to probe in front and to the sides to locate any open hatches, burned out floors or other dangers.

   D. Each man should use self-contained breathing apparatus so that he is certain of a full supply of air under all conditions.

   E. The men must move cautiously, since the foam blanket will insulate them from the fire, and they might move into the fire area without too much warning. It is for this reason that it is best for them to have a hose line, charged and ready for operation.

   F. If the men are moving in from the front of the building, the rear of the building must be adequately vented, since the foam will be pushing the superheated gases in that direction and it is dangerous to use fog streams in an enclosure without ventilation.

   G. At this stage of knowledge, we do not precisely know the effect of foam on breathing apparatus. Therefore, team relief should be provided at perhaps 10-minute intervals when wearing breathing apparatus of 30-minute rating.

# Chapter 16

# *Old Type Loft Buildings*

As long as these old commercial buildings exist, they will present fire control problems to the communities in which they are found. The cases presented are intended to emphasize basic strategy and tactics to be used in fighting fires in these structures, and to alert the fire strategist to the structural collapse possibilities associated with such fires.

**CASE 1**

*CONSTRUCTION*

The building is an old type loft, four stories high, 40 X 90 feet, and of nonfireproof construction. The interior stairs are enclosed in fire-retardant partitions. There is a bulkhead and skylight over the stairs at the roof level. There is a fire escape on the rear of the structure. Since similar buildings are contiguous, the side walls are unpierced.

Each floor has one tenant, and all the tenants are dress manufacturers. The fire loading is light to moderate throughout the building.

*FIRE SITUATION*

It is nighttime, and no flame is visible, although smoke is pushing out the third floor front windows, and smoke envelops the top floor. There is no life hazard.

*ACTION (Figure 1)*

1. The first engine company pulls up in front of fire building and

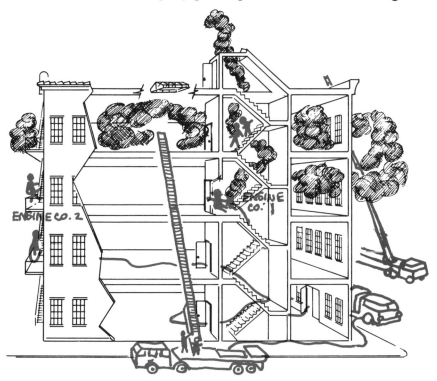

Figure 1. *These tactics have been successfully used in controlling many loft building fires for over 50 years in the loft districts of New York City.*

lays a 3-inch and a 2½-inch line. The 3-inch line is used to feed an elevated stream and the 2½-inch line is stretched up interior stairs to the third floor.

2. The ladder company positions its aerial close enough to the building so that the ladder pipe can be inserted into the windows. Personnel then proceed to the third floor. Two men are dispatched to the roof, via interior stairs, with orders to immediately return to fire floor when their mission is accomplished. Their job is to open the bulkhead door and remove or ventilate the bulkhead skylight. In the interim, doors on fourth and fire floor are forced, but then closed until return of the roof men.

3. Engine 2 is ordered to stretch a line up the interior stairs to the second floor and go to rear fire escapes on third floor. The men are told not to use water until ordered. The second ladder company performs forcible entry necessary to permit movement by Engine 2.

4. At about this time, the door to the loft on the third floor is opened. The enginemen take a prone or kneeling position so that the heat from fire area will flow above their heads. As the dense smoke starts clearing at the floor level, the hose line is advanced. At this time, the rear windows and door are opened. As the line continues to move in, the laddermen are removing any obstructions and are trying to ventilate from inside the loft.

5. When the engine company hits the body of fire on the third floor, the laddermen are ordered to the fourth floor to examine for fire extension.

### QUESTIONS

*1. All lines stretched within the fire building are 2½-inches. Why not use 1½-inch lines, for they have the advantages of faster stretching and greater mobility?*

2. *Why delay the advancement of the line on the third floor until the men return from their roof mission?*

3. *The second line is stretched up the rear fire escape to the third floor. The line is charged, but orders are issued not to use water until further instructions are given. Explain this tactical procedure.*

4. *Why delay opening and examining the fourth floor until the engine company hits the body of fire on the third floor?*

1. It is true that only smoke is showing and no flame is visible. But the critical phase of fighting this fire is at the time of ventilation. Since the fire has not vented itself, speed in stretching is not the key factor. The fire occurs at night, so the presumption is there is no life hazard. The area of the building is large and its occupancies are flammable. Once the third floor loft is opened and the roof ventilated, then, and only then, do you have full cognizance of the nature of this fire. If the fire is incipient, then an extinguisher or a 1½-inch line will suffice. On the other hand, if the fire is in the development phase, the larger streams will improve your chances for quick extinguishment. There would be no advantage for the 1½-inch line in this situation. Sometimes speed is necessary, but in this case the strategist cannot be surprised and overcome by a fire which can easily be beyond the capability of a 1½-inch line. A well-coordinated plan is the key to managing this fire situation.

2. The roof must be opened to maintain the stairway for access to the third and fourth floors. Otherwise, the smoke will mushroom and the heat will inhibit or prevent movement on the third and fourth floors. By having the men report back, you are certain of the accomplishment of their tasks. The use of the stairway provides the quickest and most certain means of roof ventilation. However, if the third floor door is forced and left open while the roof men are in the upper regions of the stairway, the smoke and heat emerging from this opening could trap them while they are trying to open or reach the bulkhead door. As long as ventilation is controlled, these procedures can be accomplished without further major development of the fire.

3. The commander must base his strategy on a potential fire development. Therefore, he wants his lines in position before the loft is ventilated. Once ventilated, the loft fire must be extinguished in a relatively short time. With the large area and combustibility of dresses, and without application of water to the seat of the fire, it is only a question of minutes

before this loft could be completely engulfed in flames. The stairway line is the major attack line. However, heat or partitioning within the loft may prevent the line's advancement. You then have two alternatives and their selection will depend on the area of greater fire involvement. Use the fire escape line if the rear of the loft is burning vigorously. If the fire breaks out in the front of building, use the elevated stream to diminish the intensity of the fire.

4. The gases of combustion will act as a suppressant to any further combustion until the fourth floor vents itself or is ventilated, and when the third floor line hits fire, some of the generated steam will permeate the fourth floor. If the fire on the third floor is of major proportions, in this type of construction the fourth floor becomes untenable. It is better, therefore, to keep the fourth floor sealed until fire has been darkened on third floor and a line has been stretched to the fourth floor.

## CONCLUSIONS

Although we have considered a number of alternatives in this fire situation, the facts presented in the case indicate that the fire would be successfully extinguished by first-alarm units. Where the floor load is not excessive, the occupancy only moderately flammable and no flame is visible from the exterior, with proper coordination of line advancement and ventilation, the fire can generally be extinguished before it reaches the stages of a roaring fire.

However, if line mobility cannot be maintained and the fire continues to burn with vigor on the third floor and extends in a major way to the fourth floor, then it is time to withdraw the companies and set up a defensive strategy. A 40 X 90-foot nonfireproof building of old-type loft construction will frequently have as its structural members unprotected cast iron columns and steel beams and girders. They will fail under severe fire conditions. Therefore, when you cannot quickly extinguish the fire, you must necessarily withdraw the companies and operate cautiously to protect their lives.

**CASE 2 (Figure 2)**

This fire originates in a four-story loft, 25 X 65 feet, of old nonfireproof construction. The interior stairs are open, but there is a fire escape on the rear of the building. The loft is used for showroom and storage purposes, but the floor load is light and the occupancy only moderately combustible.

*FIRE SITUATION ON ARRIVAL*

It is nighttime, and flames are shooting out of the third floor windows, front and rear. The upper floor is draped in smoke.

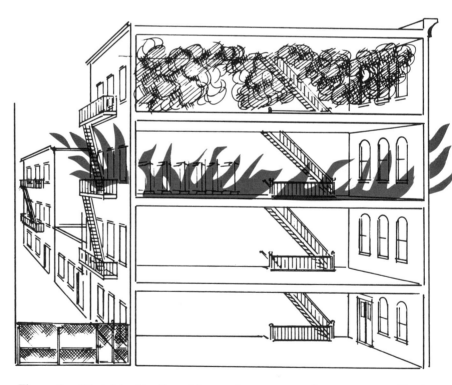

Figure 2. *Diminish this fire with exterior streams, then wage an offensive attack.*

*ACTION*

1. The fourth floor of this building is sure to light up unless heavy stream appliances are positioned to direct their streams into the upper floor. Therefore, immediately position a ladder pipe or elevating platform stream in front of the building. Direct streams into the third floor and, with streams, break windows on the fourth floor. Then flow the fourth floor.
2. Water must be immediately directed into the rear of building. Originally, use a deluge set to hit the third and fourth floors. In the meantime, stretch a line up rear fire escapes to improve stream penetration.
3. If the fire continues to extend, transmit greater alarms, protect exposures and increase the number of exterior streams.
4. On the other hand, if the fire appears to be diminishing, ventilate the roof and develop an offensive attack inside the building. When interior lines are in position, shut down exterior streams.

*QUESTION*

*In this fire situation, why does the strategy involve darkening the fire with exterior streams and then endeavoring to change the strategy to an interior attack while with this amount of fire in some loft structures, the strategy would be purely defensive?*

A 25 X 65-foot, nonfireproof building is less prone to collapse than a larger nonfireproof building. The timbers supporting the floors and floor load are anchored in the exterior side walls and do not require columns for support. Structural failure does occur in these buildings, but generally on a limited basis. Where the building must be framed out around stairways, elevator shafts and skylights, these portions of the building seem prone to collapse under heavy fire conditions. Where fire is intense, the floor beams can fail, but if the beams are of the self-releasing type, collapse is generally local and does not affect the stability of the walls.

Of course, if the fire burns without the application of water for a period of time, any building constructed largely of timber will completely disintegrate. If the floor loads are moderate to heavy, the collapse will occur much more quickly. They will do so without too much warning and with a quick chain reaction, whereby all the upper floors end in the cellar.

## CASE 3

This fire originated in a six-story, 35 X 85-foot loft building of old nonfireproof construction. It was originally designed for a light floor load occupancy, but lately it was renovated for a plumbing supply house. Bins were erected on the various floors to store plumbing fixtures. The west wall of the building is solid, but the south and east walls have shutters to protect window openings.

*FIRE SITUATION ON ARRIVAL*

It is nighttime. Smoke conditions are severe. There is no flame visible from the front of building.

*ACTION*

1. When the entrance door is opened, the engine company tries to move a line to the rear of the first floor, but since there is

no ventilation and the heat is intense, the line cannot advance.

2. The second engine company stretches a line up the interior stairs to the second floor, but the heat and smoke prevents any progress of the line.

3. In the meantime, shutters are being removed from windows at the rear on lower floors and roof is opened. When this occurs, massive fire shows.

4. Companies are immediately withdrawn from the building, heavy streams are positioned and exposures are protected.

5. In a short time, fire is showing at many front windows. Not long thereafter the roof collapses, then the rear wall, and in quick succession, the east and west walls.

Figure 3. *This type fire building can be a death trap for fire fighters. Where floor leads are heavy and fire is extensive, use a defensive strategy.*

*In this particular fire, why would the chief quickly change his strategy by withdrawing companies from the interior and developing a defensive operation?*

*ANSWER*

This situation is quite different from previous fire. The area of the building tells the chief that the probability is that the floors are supported by cast iron columns, which are unpredictable under fire conditions. On his arrival, the outward manifestations of the fire do not reveal its extent. It is only when some of the shutters have been removed and the roof ventilated that the facts of the fire become known. With old-type construction, cast iron columns, heavy floor loads, and severe fire conditions, the prediction would be for an early collapse. Under these enumerated conditions, the key word in strategy is caution.

## FURTHER CASE HISTORIES

1. A fire occurred in a six-story, brick-joist, 50 X 90-foot commercial building erected in 1890. The principal structural members of the floors and roof were wood beams supported on the first five floors by unprotected cast iron columns. The building was stocked with 800-pound rolls of paper, twine and similar products. The fire started on the fifth floor and had

extended to the sixth floor. It was a nighttime fire. Within 12 minutes of the receipt of the alarm, the building had completely collapsed. Structural failure probably originated on the fifth floor and caused the sixth floor and roof to give way. With the momentum of weight, the other floors collapsed in quick succession.

2. A few years later in a similar type building, on a Saturday afternoon, a fire started on the second floor. The deputy chief on arrival transmitted a radio report to headquarters as follows: "Fire is blowing out windows of second floor and has probably extended to the third floor." While he was giving this report, he noted fire extending up an elevator shaft and extending to all upper floors. He therefore had to modify his radio report and, while doing so, he heard the crashing of timbers and added to his report: "Internal structural collapse has started." A unique feature of this fire is that the building had a thermostatic alarm system. It did operate and the fire companies responded within two minutes. The spread of fire in old-type loft and factory buildings can be so rapid that a fully automatic sprinkler system is the only suitable method of protecting the tenants and fire fighters, because of the quick collapse possibilities.

# Chapter 17

# Grease Hood and Duct Fires

If in reviewing fires in grease ducts, the student becomes aware of the problems, he can develop the strategy and tactics to cope with these situations. We learn from the experiences of others as well as from our own experiences.

## THE WOOLWORTH BUILDING FIRE

This is a high rise structure of 60 stories. The fire started in the basement kitchen and spread via the duct to the sub-basement and upward to the roof. The New York City skyline was marred by huge clouds of smoke billowing from the roof outlet of the duct. The NYC Building Code requires that grease ducts be enclosed in fireproof assemblies for this type of structure. The duct contained the fire. Although the fire originated in the basement area, the major fire was inside the duct at the 53rd floor.

Because of the lack of cleanout and inspection openings at the sub-basement level, fire fighters had to use an oxyacetylene torch to open the steel duct for water spray application.

352

This fire clearly indicates the need to trace the duct system throughout its entire length. In tall buildings, several fans may be used in relay to remove fumes from the kitchen and expel them to the outer air at the roof. Kitchens at basement and first-floor levels may be vented by fans drawing fumes to a cellar or sub-cellar, then blowing them into a shaft or duct and, by fan relay, exhausting them at roof level. All these fans must be shut off during fire operations.

## A 21-STORY FIRE-RESISTIVE BUILDING FIRE

The fire originated in the exhaust duct over a kitchen range in the basement. The flames spread through the grease accumulations to the roof. Radiated heat from the duct fire started a fire in a storage room on the 19th floor. Smoke penetrated the upper floors. Guests on upper floors, including 188 girl students, were removed to lower floors.

The smoke from grease duct fires can be extremely irritating and dense. It can cause panic and in high rise structures, the elevators do not have adequate capacity for quick evacuation. Therefore, many of the firefighters must be assigned to guiding people to areas of refuge. The fire may be controlled with two or three 1½-inch lines, but the manpower requirements for life safety may be large. The loading of elevators must be kept within safety limits.

The fire may be in a basement, but the serious problems could well be on upper floors. Therefore, on arrival, disperse the ladder personnel throughout the building and establish a communication center to keep the commander informed of conditions on all floors.

## A 5-STORY, NONFIREPROOF MERCANTILE BUILDING FIRE

The fire started in a deep-fat fryer and extended to the grease duct. The duct extended from the first floor kitchen to the roof. The duct was enclosed in metal lath and plaster except where it passed through the roof of the building. Firemen extinguished the fire in the hood and the kitchen with a booster line.

Conduction heat ignited the rafters, which burned unnoticed in the shallow space under the roof.

Where a duct runs through a concealed space in non-fireproof construction, ladder personnel must open the space to search for fire extension. There is a reluctance to do this since the damage may appear to be unnecessary. But fires originating in ducts have spread to ceilings, partitions, roof spaces, etc., to cause losses well over a million dollars. In one such incident, three fire fighters were killed when a first-floor ceiling collapsed.

## EXHAUST FAN

A grease fire on a restaurant grill was extinguished with carbon dioxide. However, the fire had spread to the vent duct over the grill. The exhaust fan was used to clear the kitchen of smoke. The fan whipped the flames through the duct to the roof, where the overheated duct ignited the combustible roof.

If blowers are in operation on arrival, shut them down. Do not allow blowers to operate until overhauling has been completed. Then turn the blower on, if it is still operable, and look at the duct for signs of smoke. Meanwhile, lines should be in position. Extinguishment within the duct is reasonably certain if nothing occurs within 15 or 20 minutes. However, starting the blower will not reveal any smoldering material outside the duct.

If the cooking range is fed by gas, the gas must be shut off. Otherwise, steam from the fog streams may extinguish the gas burners and the escaping gas might explode. A gas shutoff lock is usually at one side of a range.

## DOUBLE CEILINGS

Overheated grease in a container ignited and the flames spread to the vent hood and grease duct. Wood furring ignited through conduction and the fire spread throughout the ceiling space. The premises had a dropped ceiling below the metal-clad original ceiling. Fire damage was extensive since the fire fighters encountered considerable difficulty in pulling the dropped ceiling and then the metal-clad ceiling to extinguish the fire.

In nonfireproof construction, the hood over the range may have to be removed to examine the concealed spaces above and behind the hood. Where a double ceiling is encountered, work from above in addition to pulling the ceiling in the restaurant. Power saws, when available, should be used to expedite opening the floor above. A 1$^1$/$_2$-inch line with a right-angle tip is useful for extinguishing fire in these concealed spaces.

## ALUMINUM DUCTS

The aluminum grease duct system extended from a vent hood over ranges on the first floor of a hotel building. The duct then rose vertically to a second-floor kitchen, where the vent from a large charcoal grill was tied in. The aluminum duct melted in some areas and collapsed at other points. The firemen needed two 2$^1$/$_2$-inch lines to knock down the fire in the roof area and they extinguished the flames inside the building with booster lines.

Aluminum is not a proper material for ducts venting kitchen ranges. It has a low melting point and will lose its tensile strength rapidly under heavy fire conditions. NFPA Standard No. 96 requires cooking vapor collection hoods be of stainless steel or copper. The ducts from the hoods must be 18 gauge or heavier steel or 20 gauge stainless steel with tight joints. Vertical risers, if located inside the building, must be enclosed in a shaft, preferably masonry, at least the equivalent of four inches of hollow clay tile.

In hotels and other structures there may be many kitchens on various floor levels, all exhausting into the primary shaft or duct. In some hotels, there are rooms adjoining these shafts. Access panels or doors to the shaft are in the closets of these rooms. Occupants, unaware of the smoke buildup within their closets, can readily be suffocated in their sleep. Therefore, the chief in charge of the fire must have the hotel management call the occupants of these rooms via the switchboard. At times, pass keys can be obtained from the management to expedite opening the rooms. In any event, procedures must be developed in cooperation with the hotel management for examination of all rooms bordering on the shaft.

**OPERATIONAL PROCEDURES**

The procedures used in fighting grease duct fires differ only with the configuration of the duct system in the building and the construction materials used in the building itself. There are four common types of duct systems and a tactical approach can be developed for each system.

*TYPE ONE (Figure 1)*

This type generally runs from first floor basement kitchens directly to the outside of the building, were it may terminate or continue on the outside of the building to the roof. If there are two or more kitchens at first floor or basement levels, the one duct invariably ventilates all the kitchens. Where the fan housing is on the roof, the fire will probably extend to the fan housing and in some cases will involve the roof covering. Where the duct runs up on the outside of the building, it may pass in close proximity to room windows. These rooms must be examined for fire extension.

Where the fire has extended throughout the duct, the first engine and ladder companies will operate in the kitchens. The second engine and ladder companies will operate above the fire and especially at the roof level.

*TYPE TWO (Figure 2)*

The duct in first floor or basement kitchens extends through a one-story, extension roof and then up the outside of the building to the main roof. The fan housing is usually on the extension roof. Where the building is very tall, an additional fan may be at the main roof level. Generally, these fires are easy to extinguish, for the fire usually stops at the fan housing on the extension roof. It rarely will extend to the duct running up to the main roof. The danger spot, of course, is the hanging ceiling in the rear of the kitchen. If opening this concealed combustible space reveals fire, quickly use power saws to open the roof itself. This will localize the fire.

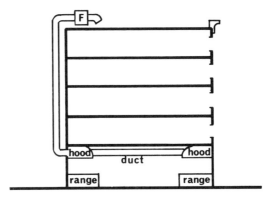

Figure 1.  *The exterior grease duct simplifies fire operations.*

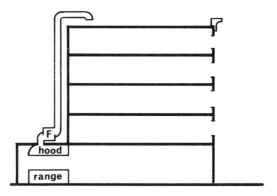

Figure 2.  *In this duct system the fire is generally confined to the system, but at times fire will extend to combustible ceiling and extension roof.*

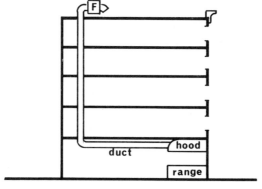

Figure 3.  *This system exposes the entire interior of the building, except when enclosed in fireproof material. Fire may extend to floors almost simultaneously while filling the building with large volumes of acrid smoke.*

The first engine and ladder companies will operate in the kitchen and on the extension roof. A 1½-inch line into the kitchen and a booster line on the extension roof will, in most cases, prove adequate. The second engine and ladder companies will operate on the other floors of the building and the roof.

*TYPE THREE (Figure 3)*

This type is frequently found in higher buildings of nonfireproof construction. Instead of running up the outside of the building, the duct pierces the many floors inside the building and vents at the roof. The fan housing is on the roof. This situation can be serious, for fire can extend in any of the ceiling spaces on any of the floors. All the ceilings will have to be opened and examined, so it is advisable to call additional ladder companies in accordance with the needs.

The first line is stretched to the kitchen area, the second line to the roof, and the third line to cover the other floors. If ladder personnel discover fire on more than one floor level, immediately call at least two more engine companies.

Fires in concealed spaces can quickly overwhelm fire forces. Opening ceilings and partitions and cockloft spaces will rapidly fatigue fire fighters. If the fire is not conquered in the early phases, it will ravage the building.

If the restaurants are occupied, the patrons can panic even under moderate smoke conditions, especially where such occupancies are in basements. Rapid evacuation is the best method to alleviate this situation. With grease fires, the smoke condition can go from moderate to severe in a short time. Therefore, all the fire fighting forces should originally be concerned with safeguarding the occupants and evacuating the premises when necessary. Fire control is secondary. When the main evacuation has been accomplished, thoroughly search all parts of the premises, particularly dressing rooms, locker rooms, lounges and kitchens.

*TYPE FOUR*

These are the exhaust systems used in fireproof buildings. The ducts from the kitchen hoods almost invariably extend to the roof through an interior shaft. In the taller buildings, two or more fans may be used in relay.

It is possible for fire to extend throughout the duct system, but this is a rarity. The fire generally does not pass the first fan and almost never beyond the second fan. However, since the duct must be traced from its point of origin to its termination, and especially through any hanging ceiling areas, the fire operation may be of long duration. Non-fireproof buildings result in fires of greater intensity, faster spread and greater life endangerment. The fire fighting in high rise structures may be less spectacular. However, examination of the duct in concealed spaces and the shaft throughout the building can test the ingenuity of any chief and the endurance of all the fire fighters.

Very often kitchens on upper floors exhaust into the primary shaft. This is a danger area and requires immediate inspection.

Where the kitchen and roof lines do not completely extinguish fire, examine along the horizontal run of the duct, since this is where the heaviest accumulation of grease collects and where the fire burns with the greatest intensity. Open the duct at this point so that water can be applied in the form of spray. The steam generation may be so vast as to envelop the firemen. Protect against this hazard by originally using limited water. Then, when an estimate of the situation has been made, further open the nozzle if necessary.

When a pot of cooking oil is burning on the stove, the application of water will result in a boil over and possibly spread the fire. $CO_2$ becomes light because of the heat of the fire and is carried away by convection currents. Furthermore, reignition can occur since the hot metal has not been sufficiently cooled. A solid stream will cause grease to erupt, spill and endanger fire fighters. A fog nozzle should be used with the control only partially cracked to reduce pressure and discharge. Originally, fog is used above the grease container and then the stream is gently lowered to sweep the top of container. This will cool the grease and the surrounding metal.

### FOG STREAMS

Use fog streams for duct, hood or shaft fires. Metal hoods and ducts become very hot, and a fog stream contacting hot metal will generate a vast quantity of steam which will be carried along the duct or shaft by the convection air currents, extinguishing fire well in advance of the point of application.

Where a line operates at the roof, shut the fog stream down in a matter of seconds. Once the flames are darkened and the metal cools, steam generation ceases and the free water then only adds to the damage.

### THE GREASE DUCT FIRE BARRIER UNIT (Figure 4)

Recognition of the grease duct fire hazard has, over the years, resulted in improved construction and safety standards aimed at preventing such fires or at least minimizing the impact of these occurrences. Among these corrective efforts are higher standards for duct metals; the use of flues similar to low temperature chimneys; separation and insulation of metal ducts and hoods from wooden construction; providing automatic or manual fire extinguishing systems; and requirements for the maintenance and cleanliness of hoods, filters ducts and ancillary parts of such systems.

One of the factors which has exacerbated the grease duct fire problem has been the generally increased height of buildings containing these systems. A system which provides an alternative to the multi-story flue, while dealing with the fire possibility, is the low temperature fire barrier. It is a combination unit which provides a water spray, grease collector and fan. As grease vapors rise from the restaurant range toward the hood, they are drawn into the fire barrier unit by the fan and cooled by a high pressure water spray. The cooled smoke and fumes are sent from the exhaust system direct to the outside atmosphere while the condensed grease is collected in a trap. Should fire occur in the hood or range area when the safety exhaust system is secured, a thermostatic device set at 450 degrees F. will set the fire barrier into action and sound the alarm.

The replacement of the multi-story flue system with one contained on one floor results in a considerable reduction in fire and smoke damage and a conservation of fire department resources.

In 1964 the combination unit was approved for use in the City of New York. Since then restaurant exhaust systems in some of the most prestigious high rise buildings have been equipped with the fire barriers.

Figure 4. *Fire barrier unit showing water spray in operation.*

# Chapter 18

# Major Oil Storage Fires

The usual fire encountered in an oil storage plant is generally controlled by the plant brigade with fixed or portable fire extinguishing equipment. The services of the local fire department are supportive and are directed toward accomplishing the objectives of the plant manager and arranging secondary defenses to assure localizing the fire.

The unusual fire a municipal fire department encounters in an oil storage plant is one that exceeds the capability of the plant brigade and rapidly develops to the status of an inferno. Fires of an intermediate stage are seldom presented. The fire is controlled simply or rages out of hand within a short period of time.

The fire department faces a difficult and hazardous condition at major oil storage fires. A large portion of available equipment will be used and the organization of fire fighting units comes rapidly under the direction of the chief of department. Heavy black smoke obliterates the sky, balls of fire rise above the ruptured or exploding tanks, gas flames appear at tank vents, and a stream of flowing, burning oil may quickly carry fire to nearby combustible construction.

Invariably these holocausts occur in older plants where many fire protection deficiencies exist. Close spacing of tanks, unprotected steel supports, inadequate foam systems, poor access roads, leaky pipes, corrosion of steel tank plates, and inoperative valves are contributing causes. The situation is sure to be aggravated because of the age of the plant and the toll time takes on old equipment.

## ORGANIZATIONAL PLAN

At a fire of this magnitude, the usual accent on speed and direct attack must be made secondary to a general plan based on attaining broad and encompassing control. The major thinking of the officer in command should be channeled in the following direction:

## COMMAND PROCEDURES

1. Establish immediate liaison with the plant manager and brigade chief. Since these men have probably been exercising command at this fire, there must be a discussion on the transfer of command responsibilities to the chief of the municipal department. This point must be clearly established. Otherwise, the plant manager and brigade chief will continue to act independently, which can lead only to ultimate confusion.

2. Establish your command post. Designate the plant manager and brigade chief as members of your staff and immediately ascertain from them the life hazard, the type of oil burning, the hazards, the exposures, the fire fighting appliances available, and the fire brigade activities. The command post should be as permanent as possible and positioned on the windward side of the fire. Careful selection will avoid moving the command post because of a boilover or other incident.

3. The plant manager will provide maps of the area, describe the layout of extinguishing systems and designate key personnel for operation of fire pumps and foam systems. He should also be required to provide guides and advisers to area and sector commanders.

4. Set your command procedures into operation. In addition to designating area and sector commanders and establishing a rigid system of walkie-talkie communication, a staff officer should be assigned in each of the following special fields of activity:
   A. Use of water
   B. Use of foam
   C. Safety of personnel
   D. Public relations
   E. Sewer problems
   F. Waterway problems

## STRATEGY

The objectives of the fire department effort must be directed toward:
1. Encirclement and containment of the fire
2. Absorption of high heat development
3. Extinguishment of individual fire sources
Whereas the last of these objectives may be left for the final stages, the first and second phases are generally inseparable.

Encirclement without absorption of heat invites a boilover and would be of value only where the exposures, topography and physical setup combine with the lack of offensive fire extinguishing capability to dictate a position of extreme withdrawal.

Absorption of heat without proper encirclement is hazardous because the attacking forces are likely to be flanked by the fire or its spread will be neglected.

Well placed, heavy caliber, water streams with reaches well in excess of 100 feet are the best attack method to accomplish encirclement and absorption simultaneously. They offer a reasonable position of defense, absorb heat and reduce flammable liquid evaporation while also serving as the foothold from which the later advancement of offensive lines can be launched.

## TACTICS OF HEAT ABSORPTION

When we think of oil fires, the concomitant thought is the use of foam. However, advanced oil storage fires demand the use of torrents of water as the key to control. Only after the major heat has been absorbed and mobile lines move into the fire area can we consider such refinements as the superiority of foam or water fog.

Water streams should originally be used on any structure or tank involved in fire or in the path of fire spread. Relief valves must be protected against heat destruction. Vent fires of serious intensity must be controlled. If allowed to impinge directly on a metal tank shell, a vent fire may cause instant failure of tank metal.

It is the heat that causes the havoc in these situations. With sufficient time and proximity to the fire, the shell of a tank may absorb sufficient Btu to melt. Flammable liquids expand when heated. If the relief vents are inadequate or do not function properly, high pressures may develop within the tank and cause a pressure rupture, showering the vicinity with burning oil. If exposed to direct heat, unprotected steel supports will fail, causing the tanks to drop, break their connections and release their contents.

Deluge sets, playpipe streams and well-positioned hand lines should, as far as practicable, be permanently anchored to permit continued operation of lines in case of quick withdrawal of personnel. Streams from ladder pipes or deck pipes should be positioned with a view to the probability of the spread of fire and the resultant need to move such apparatus.

## TACTICS OF ENCIRCLEMENT

Topography and Wind Direction—Wind and ground contours play a most important part in the development of the tactics of encirclement. If the wind is strong, the positions of the companies on the leeward side may be so remote from the main body of the fire that their streams will fall short. The spread of the fire will generally be greatest to leeward, and unfortunately this is the side of the fire where your artillery streams are least effective because of poor range. This forces the chief to concentrate his streams on flanks and windward side of the fire.

The chief is indeed fortunate if there is a congruency of wind direction and downward slope of the terrain. Should a boilover or a pipe or tank failure result in a flowing stream of boiling oil, the downward slope would become a veritable river of fire. Where this flow is different from the wind direction, the spread of fire will assume the pattern of the two contributing forces and complicate the defense procedures. At the Standard Oil Company fire in New York in September 1919, the wind and flow patterns were opposed, causing retreat after retreat and complete loss of the plant.

The best protection against such occurrences is the massing of water streams to penetrate the original fire area. This effort can take an hour or more and during this period, the chief must develop methods to cope with the probability of fire extension.

The services of building contractors, utility companies, and city and private agencies, as well as fire department and oil plant personnel, must be used to effect some of the following precautions.

1. Erecting of temporary walls, using sandbags, cinder blocks, etc.
2. Diking with sand, earth, gravel, etc.
3. Directing oil into pits, basins and ditches, or making excavations to hold the overflow.
4. Permitting oil to flow into waterways and setting up a floating boom defense to contain the oil.

There should be no hesitation in commandeering equipment to accomplish these tasks. Telephone companies, for example, can generally provide a great number of long poles which can be tied together to creat a boom to contain the flow of oil on a body of water.

## BOIL-OVERS

Flammable liquids containing water, viscous elements and fractions with a wide range of gravities and boiling points can be expected to boil over and expel a portion of the tank's contents as froth. Crude oil, fuel oil and crude naphtha are examples of such liquids while finished gasoline, kerosine, etc., are not subject to a boil-over. As many as 10 successive boil-overs have been experienced in a tank fire.

In the Whiting Refinery Fire, which was reported in the NFPA Quarterly of October 1955, the boil-over swept burning oil out of the yard and into an adjacent street. The oil then flowed along railroad tracks, destroying long lines of tank cars and box cars along with part of the tank car loading rack. Firemen suffered first, second and third degree burns during the violent eruption of the burning oil. If temporary diking had not been improvised, the burning oil probably would have reached buildings outside the plant.

The time of the boil-over depends on the depth of the oil and the rate at which the heat wave progresses to the water in the bottom of the tank. When close enough to the tank, a temperature indicator can be used on tanks to indicate progress of the heat wave. When indicator paint is unavailable, water thrown on the outside of the shell will indicate progress of a heat wave.

Estimate the expected time of a boil-over. It may be possible to erect emergency dikes. They should be located at least 50 feet from a tank. Plowing the ground to partially break the velocity of flow of the burning oil is often a desirable measure.

The occurrence of a boil-over is usually preceded by a marked brightening of the flames for a period of a few minutes. The safety crew should be posted to watch for these warnings so that men can seek positions of safety within a minute or two. By the time the boil-over occurs, it is too late, for then the oil will be thrown from the tank and form a wave which will have considerable velocity. Since more surface oil is now exposed to the fire, the flame will be spectacular and take the form of an inverted cone, rising 1000-feet high and perhaps as much as 1000-feet across at the top.

There is another type of overflow, which is termed a slopover. It may occur anytime during a fire. The slopover is due to an increase in oil volume because of the thermal expansion of the oil or violent boiling due to the presence of some water at the top of the tank. The outage of the oil will intensify the fire and increase the oil flow problems, but its degree is minor compared to a boil-over.

Again, the key to control of a boil-over is found in preventing prolonged fire development. The estimate of time of a boil-over will depend on the rate of burning and the depth of liquid. In most cases, preliminary estimates will determine a safe period during which efforts can be directed toward heat reduction and plans for encirclement.

## EXPOSURES

The neighboring occupancies of tank farm areas are often similarly large and hazardous. The remoteness of a few thousand feet may shrink rapidly at a major oil fire. In addition to a boil-over or flowing oil fire, the conventional exposure hazards of radiation, convection, and sparks or brands are always present. A change in wind must be anticipated and areas covered on all sides of the fire.

A chief and a number of fire companies may be required to cooperate with the fire brigade of each occupancy.

Laddermen should inspect exposed building on adjoining property and buildings still accessible in the tank farm area, closing windows and shutters, moving stock back from exposed walls, and activating fire pumps for sprinkler and standpipe systems. These are usual procedures in protecting an exposure, but if there is a further probability of fire spread, then these additional precautions can be taken:

(a) Permanently anchor streams on roof to flow the roof and to spray gravity standpipe tank supports and the wooden parts of any tank.

(b) Ventilate the unexposed side of any building to prevent buildup of heat as well as the operation of all sprinkler heads.

(c) Flow the other floors of the building and, especially, spray drums, tanks, etc. that may rupture under heated conditions.

(d) Set up street deluge sets that can be operated after men withdraw. These streams will hit the cornice of a building and the water will flow down the building facing.

Since you cannot fully predict the outbreak and development of these fires, the chief must take steps before their occurrence to have nearby residences and buildings evacuated, roadways cleared around the perimeter, and waterways constantly checked for flowing oil.

An additional exposure hazard of flowing combustible liquid is the sewers in the area. The agency in charge of sewers must be advised to maintain surveillance and remove covers to vent below-ground waterways. The sewer may terminate in a sewage disposal plant and this building must be kept under observation.

## WATER SUPPLY

The staff officer assigned to water supply will begin the survey of the water problems in the earliest stages of the fire. He must gather information on the following:

(a) Opening of valves to increase flow in the hydrant system
(b) Location of large size mains
(c) Availability of large diameter hose
(d) Feasibility of relay operations
(e) Locations for drafting
(f) Positions for fireboat operations

The fighting of previous oil refinery fires indicates that 18,000 to 20,000 gpm of water are generally a minimum requirement and demands often exceed 50,000 gpm. Oil plants generally are on the outer perimeter of a city. The municipal water supply system may consist of a single feeder main with secondary mains of relatively small diameter. If the water system in the oil storage plant is supplied directly from these mains or if the private system fails, it will be a difficult task to supply the heavy water demands of this type fire.

Fortunately, the location of a plant on the outskirts of the city often presupposes a position along a waterfront. Fireboats offer their finest value under these circumstances, but drafting with available pumpers must be considered immediately as the response of a boat is usually slow and in many cases fireboats are not available. For these reasons, pumper drafting sites must be pre-fire planned and drills conducted to ensure effective operation.

Before the fire reaches its full momentum, there is a tendency to use water streams fed from the water tanks of nearby exposed buildings. Initially, this may appear advantageous, but in the long run this procedure may lead to the loss of the exposed building. The fire protection facilities within a building are designed for its protection. If the water supply from the sprinkler, standpipe or suction tanks is exhausted, that building may be defenseless when it is threatened.

## FOAM

While the heavy exterior streams are trying to reduce the heat intensity, the staff officer assigned to foam operations will program the collection of all available foam supplies, the method of generating foam and the manner of application to particular situations.

A reserve supply of foam should be gathered in as great a quantity as possible. Oil storage depots, foam suppliers, other fire departments and all other available sources should be canvassed. It is poor policy to start an application of foam before sufficient quantity is available to build up a heavy blanket. Heat will dissipate thin foam coverings and divergent water streams will negate foam effectiveness.

Some stream appliances can propel foam streams more than 200 feet. This may permit the use of foam as an ally to water streams to blanket a trench, cover a gasoline spill, protect the underside of a pier or cover an oil pit fire. Proper coordination of foam and water streams is essential in such cases.

## SAFETY OFFICER

The selection of a safety officer will be one of the most careful judgments of the officer in command. A chief of high rank, broad experience and an excellent understanding of fire safety must be chosen. He should be assigned sufficient specialized assistance, for his responsibility is broad and includes the protection of civilian as well as fire personnel. He should work closely with a representative of the plant manager.

The safety officer should coordinate with the officer in command in carrying out the following objectives:
1. Evacuation of residences and buildings exposed to hazards. Fire personnel can assume responsibility for immediate hazards, plant supervisors for the general plant area, and the police for adjacent exposures.

2. Intelligent survey of probable hazards, such as topographical and windward spread and the possibility of a boil-over. This will constitute the main areas of his activity.

To accomplish a safe attitude in this regard, he must consider methods of:

(a) Quick, safe retreat for firemen
(b) Arrangement of second and third lines of defense
(c) Voice amplification to alert personnel
(d) Removal of obstructions, such as wire fences, etc.
(e) Lighting and laddering of paths of retreat
(f) Fire watchers for warning of slopover or boil-over
(g) Fire shields for personnel exposed to heat
(h) Provisions for full fire clothing for members.

If the heavy streams are not reaching and cooling the main body of fire, the secondary lines of defense will have to be reinforced. The safety officer will likely recommend retreat and the officer in command will be strongly influenced by his opinions.

## CASE FIRE (Figure 1)

To reaffirm the proposition that large oil storage depot fires can be controlled if adequate water supply facilities are available and can be brought into play, the following description of a fire is presented for review.

This fire occurred May 10, 1962. It was the largest oil fire in New York City since 1919. The fire was brought under control within three hours. The drawing shows the layout of the plant.

Fire originated in a pipe trench at tank 1. The piping of this tank quickly failed and 50,000 gallons of gasoline continued to feed fire in the trench. To this was added 42,000 gallons of No. 2 fuel oil from tank 16. The fire quickly spread to the pump house, truck loading rack, warehouse and pier. The warehouse was filled with drums of all types of petroleum products. Immediately to the east was another storage plant, whose vent pipes were already burning. The wind was driving the fire toward this close and serious exposure. In addition, fire was spilling on and spreading over the waters of the nearby waterway and threatening to ignite pilings and bulkheads on the opposite shore of the narrow channel.

Approximately 30 engine companies were called to the scene of this disaster. They were positioned to encircle the fire and to protect the opposite shore of the channel. Time and again the land companies pressed in from the south in the direct path of the wind-driven fire and from the east and west flanks of the fire area. The channel was on the north side of the fire area. The

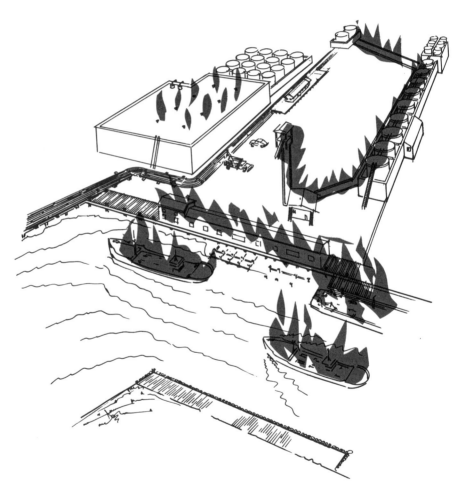

Figure 1. *The many high capacity, long range monitors of the fireboats delivered sufficient water to cool the fire area in a relatively short period of time and thus permitted foam lines to enter the fire area and complete extinguishment.*

companies were repeatedly driven back by explosions, intense heat and flame. At times, positions had to be abandoned because of convection currents and the buildup of radiated heat. The land units did not have adequate artillery to control the heat buildup and therefore, the offensive movements were doomed to failure.

After 1 hour and 43 minutes, a fireboat arrived at the scene and shortly thereafter, two additional fireboats reinforced the marine operation. Each fireboat was capable of delivering approximately 15,000 gpm, through five monitors, each with a 3-inch tip. Each monitor was able to deliver approximately 3,000 gpm and the stream range was from 300 to 400 feet. These streams readily controlled the floating oil fire, darkened the fire on the piers and in the warehouse, and sufficiently cooled the entire area to permit land units to move mobile lines into the fire area. With fog and foam streams, the last remaining pockets of fire were extinguished. The fire was brought under control 1 hour and 16 minutes after the arrival of the fireboats. The main body of fire was under control within minutes of the start of streams from the first boat.

## CASE 2 (Figure 2)

In Linden, N.J., on Dec. 5, 1970, the Humble Oil Refinery rocked from a powerful explosion. The sky was illuminated. Chief Frank J. Miklos was in command of another man-made disaster. There were many oil refineries and other large industrial complexes in Linden. So the chief and his fire personnel were attuned to these extraordinary catastrophes.

A photograph of the fire visualizes the vast area and intensity of the fire at the time of arrival of the first companies. However, within 2½ hours the fire was localized to two major areas and within eight hours, all major fires were extinguished. Large fixed monitor nozzles were one of the principal features of the fire protection facilities for this plant. The operation of these monitors materially assisted in extinguishing the fire and cooling the exposures. The water supply was excellent. The hydrant system in the yard was fed by salt water through three electrically driven pumps of 3,750, 2,600 and 2,500-gpm capacity.

Figure 2. *In Linden, N.J., on-site monitors supplied the needed massive water streams.*

### CONCLUSION

Chiefs from other cities and communities may properly ask how they can cope with major oil refinery fires without the assistance of fireboat streams or large capacity, remotely controlled, fixed monitors and when they are limited to streams with a range of 100 feet. The answer is that no fire can be controlled unless the cooling effects of the water application are greater than the generation of heat by the fire. It just cannot be done.